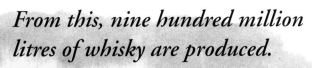

From this, nine hundred million litres of whisky are produced.

This is the story of that water...
and that whisky...

*W*hisky on the *R*ocks

Aquavitae, the water of life, is the universal term used for a distillate of fermented cereals. In the gaelic translation of this — *uisge beatha* — we hear the origin of the word *whisky*.

Of all the ingredients that are combined to produce whisky, the effects of different types of water on the final product is the most mysterious and least understood factor. The aim of this book is to lift the curtain a little and explore the origins of the water used in the production of malt whisky. Whether you are out in the *glens* or comfortably in your armchair with a glass (or two) let us help you to visualise the location and the environment that have contributed to the production of the liquid in the glass before you. In an age where the environmental lobby grows ever stronger, whisky stands out as probably one of the 'greenest' of all drinks. Crafted from barley, untreated water and yeast, the spirits of today are

2 The peat fire below the malting floor.

the result of 150 years' experience of legal (and illegal) distilling.

Water has many roles: it is extremely important in the creation of the spirit that will become whisky; it is needed to prepare the spirit for sale, and it is recommended as an aid to the full appreciation of the finished product.

There are two types of whisky: *malt,* made solely from malted barley and distilled in copper pot stills; and *grain,* produced in large volumes from a process of continuous distillation of the liquor resulting from the fermentation of several types of unmalted grain and some malted barley. *Blended* whiskies are made from unique combinations of many malts and a large base of grain spirit.

We are particularly concerned with *Single Malt* whiskies (those from an individual

malt whisky distillery) but the reader should note that in recent years a few *Single Grains* have started to appear and extending one's study to these is to be recommended.

In principle, the malt whisky-making process is simple, comprising a brewing phase and a distillation phase. In the first stage, barley is sprinkled with water to encourage its germination. This starts the complicated chemical processes that break down the *starch* to form *sugar*. After a few days, when the shoots have started to appear, the grain is heated up and the germination process is halted. The barley is then said to be *malted*. In the past, distilleries usually malted their own barley but nowadays most purchase barley

3 Strong fermentation in a wooden washback.

malted to their specific requirements from large malting plants elsewhere. Only a few use the traditional malting floor (1)

1 The traditional malting floor.

4 Pot stills made of copper produce the distillate.

different in every distillery all have a characteristic onion shape. The vapour of alcohol and other complex aromatics rises up the tall necks of the stills to condense and then be collected. In most distilleries the process is repeated once, though in a very few, triple distillation produces what is claimed to be an even purer and cleaner spirit. The cooled distillate is run off into oak casks which may once have held sherry or bourbon, and stored in warehouses to mature; by this stage the spirit is about 60% alcohol.

By law no whisky can be sold unless it has been matured for at least three years. *Scotch Whisky* is strictly defined as a spirit which has been matured in oak casks (5), in Scotland, for at least three years. Most malt whiskies will have matured for much longer than the minimum period, 10 to 20 years not being unusual. Whisky that is to be sold as a Single

Malt will have matured for all or most of its life at the distillery, but if the malt is for blending it may have been transported to the major bonded warehouses of central Scotland for maturation.

Except for a few casks that are sold to private companies and societies, the whisky that is to be bottled is reduced, by the addition of water, to between 40 and 45% alcohol prior to bottling.

There are therefore four main variables in the whisky-making process: the *peating* of the malted barley, the *shape of the stills* (particularly the height of the necks), the *type of casks* used for the maturation and the *water* used in the mashing process. We concentrate on the last.

A particular feature of the malting process is that *peat smoke* from the heating fires (2) may be allowed to pass through the barley. The amount of peating gives a level of smokiness (the *peat reek*) to the grain that is carried right through into the finished product.

The barley is ground to a coarse flour, the *grist*, which is mixed with water and then *mashed* (boiled) in large copper vessels to extract all the sugars. This liquid, the *wort*, is then cooled and put into wooden or stainless steel tanks called *washbacks* (3) and after the addition of yeast, fermentation takes place. The result, at about 9% alcohol, is a strong unhopped beer-like liquid referred to as *pot ale*.

The pot ale is then distilled by heating it in large copper stills (4) and although

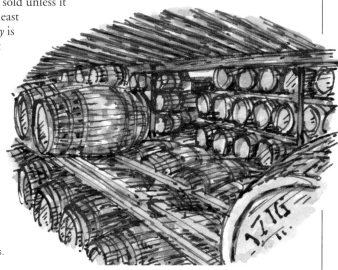

5 Whisky maturing in casks.

Whisky on the Rocks

The presence of water has always controlled the siting of distilleries, because not only is there a requirement for reliable supplies of clean, fresh, process water but also large volumes are needed for cooling purposes. Most distilleries are sited on the banks of streams or rivers. In the past these were the source of the process waters, but nowadays, particularly in areas where population and land usage has increased, it is not unusual for the water to be collected higher up in the hills and then piped to the distillery, sometimes over a distance of several kilometres. The original streams can still provide waters for cooling. In areas that are intensively farmed, or are close to large centres of population, many of the shallow or surface water sources are no longer usable at all and deeper boreholes or the public water supply have to be used. Such a change in supply can mean water of a different chemistry has to be used and this can have a significant effect on the whisky produced.

The primary source of water is rain, but what happens to rainwater before its arrival at the distillery affects its *chemistry* and thus the uniqueness of the resulting malt whisky. The rain may end up as a stream or river, in a loch or a reservoir, coming from the rock as deep or shallow boreholes (5), or as a spring high on a hillside (1, 2).

If it falls on bare mountains made of crystalline rocks it will flow rapidly downhill as streams. This water has little chance to interact with the underlying rocks and often has a low mineral content. It will be acid and soft.

1 A spring line forms where the water table intersects the land surface.

2 Water is forced to the surface because it cannot pass through an impermeable layer.

On the other hand if the strata are more permeable, or have many joints and fractures (4), the rain will percolate into and through the rock (3), dissolving it and increasing the water's *mineral* content. Limestones and sandstones, for example, yield waters rich in carbonates or sulphates; such waters will be neutral or slightly alkaline and hard.

'Soft water, through peat, over granite' was the traditional and still oft-quoted view of the best water for distilling. Remarkably, out of the 100 or so single malt whiskies, less than 20 use water that fits this description. What is certain is that the water must be crystal clear; it must be pure, and the source must be reliable.

the pioneering spirits of its geologists, beginning with James Hutton, the *founder of modern geology*. Scottish localities have given their names to a chemical element *(strontium)*, minerals *(cairngorm, leadhillite, mullite, tobermorite)* and rocks *(appinite, kentallenite, mugearite)*: exports of significance, if not as famous as the whiskies!

3 Water flows through joints and cracks in rocks and appears at the edge of a valley filled with impermeable clay.

There is no prescribed way to appreciate fully the flavour of the whisky, but it is generally agreed by the experts that the addition of a little water releases the aromatics and increases the perception of both taste and smell. The ideal is to be able to use the water from which the whisky was made.

4 A fault breaks the rocks and creates a channel of easy flow to the surface.

Several distilleries have taken the lead from Glen Grant, which in Victorian days kept spirits by the distillery dam and allowed a special tasting for favoured clients. If you are ever lucky enough to get such an opportunity, seize it with both hands, but if not, try to use a pure, unsparkling Scottish mineral water to dilute your whisky.

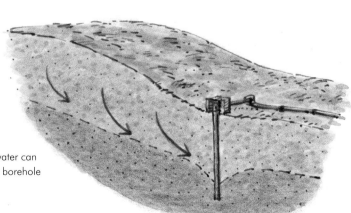

5 Underground water can be tapped by a borehole or well.

Your tour is about to begin, but first let us look at Scotland's geology, famed throughout the world for its variety and

Whisky on the Rocks

(Of Scotland) 'Your country consists of two things, stone and water.'
Dr Samuel Johnson, 1773.

Through the science of geology we can study and interpret the rocks that make up the Earth and we are fortunate that Scotland possesses a great variety of these. Many of the great pioneers of geology cut their teeth — and partook of many a dram — in the hills and valleys, on the mountains and islands. There is a 2800 million-year geological pageant, the flavour of which you will taste in these pages.

Before going into details, let us give a general perspective. The most notable features of Scotland are the large *faults** which run across the country from the northeast to the southwest and divide it into blocks (1, 2). This NE–SW grain to the country originated during great events in its geological history.

The most southerly fault, the *Southern Upland Fault*, separates Ordovician and Silurian rocks of the Southern Uplands from the rocks of the Midland Valley. The Southern Uplands block consists of grey slates and sandstones.

The Midland Valley, the **Deep South** of our book, is a *rift valley** floored by fertile plains on Devonian and Carboniferous rocks. To the north across the *Highland Boundary Fault*, these give way dramatically to the intensely folded and *metamorphosed** Dalradian rocks of our **Grampian Highlands** and **Argyll Islands** chapters.

* Basic geological terms are explained in the Geological Glossary *(page 71)*.

1 Map showing main geological faults, rocks (see below) and the regions covered by present book chapters *(in bold)*.

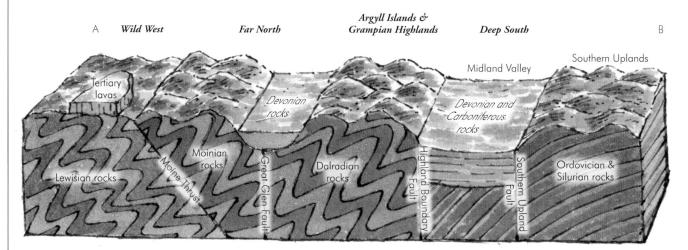

2 Schematic section through Scotland cut along the line A–B in 1 *(above)* showing rocks, faults and the regions covered by the present book chapters *(in bold type)*.

Further north, the Dalradian *schists* of the Grampian block are separated from the older Moinian rocks by the *Great Glen Fault*. In the northwest, this Moinian block is pushed over Lewisian rocks as old as 2900 million years in places.

In the far northeast, and forming our **Far North** chapter, are the Devonian Old Red Sandstones of the *Orcadian Basin*.

Just to the south of Lewis is Skye, one of the very 'young' volcanic islands, followed southwards by Mull and Arran and the plains of Antrim in Northern Ireland. In these localities the lavas and ancient volcanoes are 'only' 60 million years old and form our **Wild West** chapter.

Geologists always start their reports by describing the oldest rocks at the bottom of their geological column. Our whisky trail will do the same. We shall sample the delights both of the whisky and of the rocks through which its waters percolate by ascending our column (3)

Come with us then, on a tour of Scotland, starting with the ancient Argyll Islands and finishing in the 'young' volcanic islands of the Wild West. Absorb the scenery and sample the multitude of unique distillates. In a book of this size we cannot offer you detailed descriptions of every distillery, though all are mentioned. Our aim is to highlight geological and scenic variety; so, whether you are sitting in your armchair at home with a range of malts, or travelling through Scotland, turn the page now and have your perspectives changed for ever.

3 A geological column for *Whisky on the Rocks*.

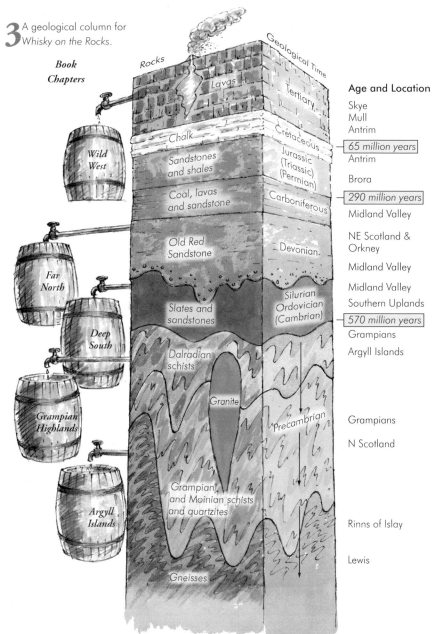

Book Chapters

Rocks

Geological Time

Age and Location

Skye
Mull
Antrim

65 million years
Antrim

Brora

290 million years
Midland Valley

NE Scotland & Orkney

Midland Valley

Midland Valley
Southern Uplands

570 million years
Grampians

Argyll Islands

Grampians

N Scotland

Rinns of Islay

Lewis

Wild West

Far North

Deep South

Grampian Highlands

Argyll Islands

Lavas

Chalk

Sandstones and shales

Coal, lavas and sandstone

Old Red Sandstone

Slates and sandstones

Dalradian schists

Granite

Grampian and Moinian schists and quartzites

Gneisses

Tertiary

Cretaceous

Jurassic
(Triassic)
(Permian)

Carboniferous

Devonian

Silurian
Ordovician
(Cambrian)

Precambrian

The Argyll Islands

*'Westering home with a song in the air...
...at hame wi' my ain folks in Islay.'*
Sir Hugh Roberton.

The Argyll Islands of the Inner Hebrides lie to the northwest of the Kintyre Peninsula, off the west coast of the Scottish mainland. Several islands form the group, and although all have fascinating rocks, only two are of serious interest to the determined whisky traveller.

These are the two largest: Islay and Jura. With a total population of about 4200 (Islay 4000 and Jura 200) they boast seven working distilleries and a further two which are currently mothballed.

Taken together, Islay and Jura form an excellent starting point for our journey of discovery, offering, in a relatively small area, high mountains, huge peat bogs and gentle limestone country. The western and southwestern coasts are exposed to

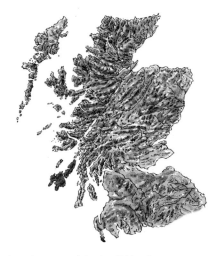

Location map of the Argyll Islands.

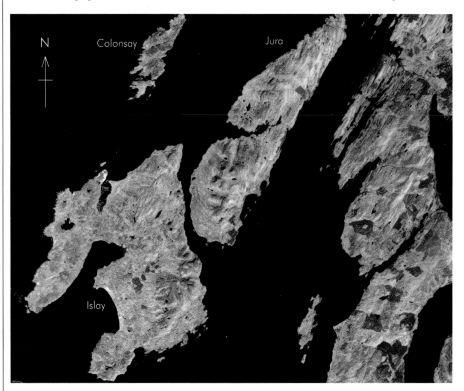

1 Satellite image showing Islay, Jura and Colonsay and part of the mainland. This false colour infrared image highlights the physical structure and vegetation: moors and peat bogs are bluish; natural forests and agricultural land pink-orange; and conifer plantations brown. Water is black. Turn the page upside down for a better appreciation of the relief. *(BGS enhanced satellite image)*.

the Atlantic storms; the east-facing shores are relatively sheltered. The hill features can be seen on the satellite image of the islands and are a direct expression of the geology of the area (1). A very striking feature is the NE–SW-trending grain of the land across southern Islay, Jura and the mainland. Within this rocky grain, a spine of high ground, made of hard, white *quartzite* rock, runs northeastwards from the southern tip of Islay (The Oa) through to Jura, broken only by the Sound of Islay, along which the rock spine forms high mountains which rise from the sea. On Jura, it forms the mighty Paps which give the island its distinctive skyline.

The southeast coasts of both islands are characterised by strings of islets and inlets parallel to the main rock trend, within which shelter five of the island distilleries.

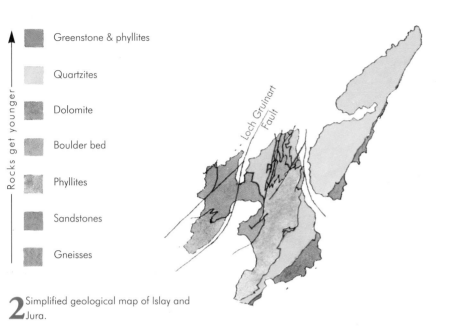

Rocks get younger →

- Greenstone & phyllites
- Quartzites
- Dolomite
- Boulder bed
- Phyllites
- Sandstones
- Gneisses

Loch Gruinart Fault

2 Simplified geological map of Islay and Jura.

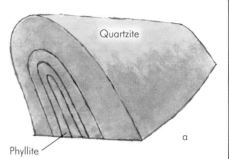

Quartzite

Phyllite

a

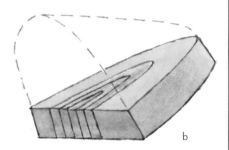

b

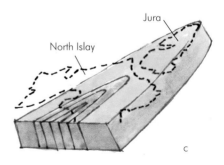

Jura

North Islay

c

3 Rocks were folded into a plunging anticline (a) and then eroded (b). Islay and Jura were formed from this structure (c).

The far west of Islay is distinctly different. It is in fact separated geologically from the rest of the island by a major break in the rocks along which substantial earth movement has occurred in the past. This feature is known as the *Loch Gruinart Fault* (2).

Almost all of the rocks to the east of the Loch Gruinart fault on Islay and the whole of Jura were formed in *late Precambrian* times (800–600 million years ago) and make up part of the large division of rocks called the *Dalradian*, named after the ancient Scots Kingdom of Dalriada which was centred on these islands and the adjoining mainland.

At the end of this period, around 600 million years ago, the Dalradian rocks were folded into an arch *(anticline)* which plunges gently to the northeast (3). As this happened, the heat and pressure that were generated caused the rocks to recrystallise, a process termed *metamorphism*. This geological activity is an early stage of the *Caledonian Orogeny* which affected most of Scotland.

Our geological journey through the islands will follow around the structure of the anticline. The water sources for the distilleries are as varied as the geology and include surface run-off, local springs, reservoirs and rivers. The whiskies produced vary as widely, ranging from highly distinctive, pungent, full-bodied types through to altogether lighter and paler distillates.

The Argyll Islands

Of whisky 'A torchlight procession marching down your throat.' J L O'Sullivan, attrib.

The starting point for our whisky tour is Port Ellen on Islay's south coast which sits on the southeast side of the main arch or anticline. Here, erosion of rocks with differing hardnesses has resulted in the formation of the enclosed bay which makes Port Ellen an important ferry port.

The sheltered southeast coast which runs from here to Ardtalla and beyond is extremely beautiful. The landforms reflect the geology of the area. Glistening white mountains of quartzite, with little or no vegetation, rise above the hilly coastal strip which is more fertile, though in places very poorly drained; it contains areas of peat interspersed with rough pasture and woodland. These hills conform to the NE–SW Caledonian trend giving rise to a serrated landscape with ridges of hard, greenish, metamorphosed igneous rocks (*greenstones*) raised above much softer greeny blue slaty rocks, known as *phyllites*.

The igneous rocks originally forced their way through the strata as fluid magma.

On the coast itself (1) the erosion of the softer phyllites has resulted in many small sheltered bays, three of which have become the sites of the distilleries which produce the heavy, pungent, phenolic whiskies characteristic of, and unique to, Islay; from west to east these are Laphroaig, Lagavulin and Ardbeg (3)

The protection provided by these bays was important at a time when grain, coal and whisky were all brought in or taken out by boat (2)

3 Oblique sketch view of the southeast coast of Islay showing the water sources in the quartzite hills.

Laggan Bay

Port Ellen

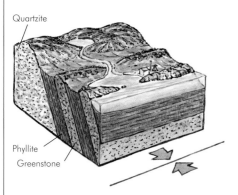

1 Geological cross-section of the southeast coast of Islay.

Quartzite

Phyllite
Greenstone

2 Most distilleries were supplied by steam coasters, known as *puffers*.

The distilling waters used by all three distilleries come from small lakes or *lochans* high in the quartzite hills, from which they descend as small streams crossing the phyllites and greenstones and their peaty covering.

The highest source, at around 250 metres, is Loch Uigeadail which supplies **Ardbeg**. Water leaves the loch as a stream and flows south over quartzite, eventually becoming the Ardilistry River. However, much of the water is diverted from the river into Loch Iarnan, excavated out of the thick peat which lies on top of the phyllites, before flowing down the Ardbeg Burn to the distillery.

Lagavulin (*picture, page 18*) takes its water from the Sholum Lochs on the southern slopes of Beinn Sholum, crossing similar rock types until it is intercepted by a dam about a kilometre north of the distillery and is piped from there.

Leorin
Lochs

Loch
Uigeadail

Sholum Lochs

Loch Iarnan

Kilbride Dam

Lagavulin

Laphroaig

Ardbeg

Texa

The **Laphroaig** source is a burn, originating to the west of the Sholum Lochs. The water is held in the Kilbride Dam about a kilometre north of the coast.

The quartz rocks of the mountains, and the peaty lowlands make the waters highly acidic, but as most of the water moves by surface flow there is little opportunity for it to react with the rocks beneath. As a result the mineral content is very low.

All these distilleries have similar sources and it is noticeable that all have similar flavour characteristics. However, the powerful phenolic taste and smell is mainly the result of the heavy peating of the barley during malting.

Port Ellen distillery, now mothballed, drew its water from the Leorin lochs in the southern quartzite hills, though this water did not pass over any of the softer, more soluble rocks. Its whisky, more difficult to sample nowadays, is of a heavy type similar to the other south coast malts.

Phyllite drystone wall, inland from Laphroaig.

The Argyll Islands

1 The Isle of Jura Distillery with the Market Loch to the left and the Paps in the distance.

Market Loch (Loch a'Bhaile–Mhargaidh) before tumbling down through peaty lowlands to a dam near the distillery. Although by no means as smoky as its Islay counterparts, the lightly peated spirit has a lively and characteristic nature.

Leaving the side of the anticline and moving north and west around its core, we recross the Sound of Islay to the coast just north of Port Askaig. Here in a sheltered bay is the distillery of **Caol Ila** (3). Geologically we have moved closer to the centre of the fold, to older rocks.

Caol Ila takes its water from a source close to the distillery, Loch Nam Ban (the Torrabolls Loch) in the hills immediately behind. This loch lies within one of the most interesting rock formations in the whole of the Highlands: the *Port Askaig Tillite*. A good place to see this rock is on the coast north of the distillery and at Port Askaig itself. It is a hard brown sandstone with scattered pebbles of pink granite (2), thought to have been dropped from the underside of melting icebergs: evidence of a period of glaciation about 650 million years ago seen on other continents in rocks of the same age.

Some scientists think this worldwide glaciation resulted from a cosmic collision and was also the 'spark' which kindled the rapid evolution of advanced

Following the eastern side of Islay Anticline towards the northeast, our journey takes us over the water to Jura.

Here the quartzites, which we saw in the hills of southern Islay, make up almost the whole of the island and are best observed in the mighty Paps of Jura.

Most of the phyllites and greenstones disappear into the Sound of Jura but

sufficient of them remains to define a coastline of ridges and bays stretching the length of the island from Ardfin to beyond Barnhill, where George Orwell wrote *Nineteen Eighty Four*.

The **Isle of Jura** distillery (1), is situated at the southern end of Small Isles Bay, named after its islands of greenstone. The water source is in the southern quartzite hills where it collects in the

12

life forms seen in the Cambrian Period, 570 million years ago.

On the coast about a kilometre north of Caol Ila is the **Bunnahabhain** (Bonahaven) distillery, which is unique amongst those on the island in that its spring water is piped directly from the rocky hills without passing over any peat or glacial deposits. The rocks from which the spring rises are calcium-magnesium carbonates *(dolomites)* and one would expect a more mineralised water and thus a different flavour. This is indeed the case as evidenced by the light clean taste of the whisky.

The creamy-coloured dolomite is another fascinating rock because it

contains fossilised *stromatolites* (4), one of the oldest and most primitive forms of life. These were large mounds of algae which grew in shallow, warm waters to form reef-like 'mats'. They existed prior to the explosion of life on Earth in the Cambrian and can still be found in the tropical seas today!

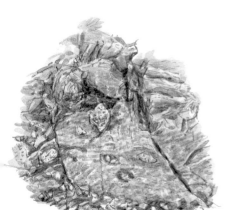

2 Pink granite boulders in the Port Askaig Tillite along the Bunnahabhain road: evidence for an ancient ice age.

4 Stromatolites on the coast east of Bunnahabhain: early life forms, rarely preserved.

The stromatolites are well exposed to the south of the distillery for a distance of almost 200 metres around the rocky headland of Rubh'a'Mhill.

Scrambling around the cliffs will also bring you face to face with a shipwrecked fishing boat below the eerie cliffs. Less-accessible exposures occur on the far north and northeast coast of Islay.

3 Caol Ila Distillery from Jura.

The Argyll Islands

'And malt does more than Milton can,
To justify God's ways to man.'
A E Housman, *A Shropshire Lad.*

Nowhere is far from the sea on a small island and **Bowmore** distillery in central Islay is no exception. What is remarkable, however, is that its water is taken from the principal river of the island, the Laggan, which rises in the high hills that overlook the Sound of Islay on the east coast (1). This is about as far from Bowmore as it is possible to get on Islay, almost 16 kilometres away.

Central Islay coincides with the core of the Islay Anticline and the phyllites, limestones and dolomites that occur here are the oldest of the Dalradian rocks we have come across so far. Being softer than the surrounding quartzites they have been eroded by the Laggan to form a wide fertile bowl opening westwards and lined with river alluvium and glacial deposits.

About halfway along the course of the Laggan, near to Mulindry (2), some of the water is diverted into a man-made channel, or *lade*, which then flows by gravity for a distance of nearly eight kilometres to the distillery. This is a remarkable feat of engineering because the water falls only about 25 metres (3)

The journey from source to distillery is one of major and sudden contrasts as the differing rocks are crossed. Here indeed is a cross-section of the island. High up, small streams tumble off the heathery quartzite hills and join up to form a river flowing past beautiful limestone country of rounded outcrops, springy grass and, in the spring, patches of lemon primroses. Further down, the valley is filled with glacial deposits and alluvium, and the river meanders gently between grassy banks which in early summer are brightly coloured with the reds, blues, yellows and whites of wild flowers. As the river continues to flow southwestwards towards the sea, the lade branches off westwards across peaty lowlands and finally turns northwards crossing grey sandstones before reaching the distillery.

1 Bowmore water, from source to distillery. Looking north we see the whole of the Laggan valley and the lade which branches off from the river and runs all the way to Bowmore.

Loch Indaal

BRID[G]

BOWMORE

Bowmore

the Lade

River Laggan

2 The banks of the Laggan near Mulindry.

These grey sandstones of Bowmore have always posed problems for geologists. Some think they are Dalradian strata whilst others suggest they are much older. Even more puzzling is the fact that they do not appear to have been metamorphosed.

The water source is thus a mixture of the quartzites of the southeast and the limestones and sandstones of the north, and the whisky is a similar blend. It is peaty and pungent, though more subtle than the whiskies of south coast; pale and light but not as light as the northeast coast.

14

Sound of Islay

Bowmore and Laphroaig are the only distilleries on Islay that now malt barley on their own malting floors. The others use the central maltings at the old Port Ellen distillery or bring it in from the mainland.

Southwards from Bowmore, for over 20 kilometres to the very outskirts of Port Ellen, stretches an immense, low-lying peat bog, the Duich Moss, which is an important natural habitat for rare plants, birds and animals. It is also the source of peat for both the distilleries and the islanders (4), though since the area is so vast and the peat so deep there is no conflict of interests.

3 The Bowmore Lade looking east.

4 Cut and stacked peat on the Duich Moss.

In an acknowledgement of the saying that the best water with which to dilute one's *dram* is that from which it was distilled, the pale brown, peaty water close to the Bowmore source has been bottled and was sold commercially as *Islay Water*.

The Argyll Islands

1 Bruichladdich Distillery and Beinn Tart a'Mhill looking across Loch Indaal from Blackrock.

Whether looking at the map or standing on the shores of Loch Indaal, it is obvious that, both physically and geologically, the far west of Islay, the Rinns, is different from the rest of the island. Indeed in earlier times when sea levels were higher it would have been a separate island.

The major fault which separates the Rinns from the rest of Islay passes offshore up Loch Indaal and continues northwards across the narrow neck of land to pass into Loch Gruinart.

The rocks of the Rinns fall into two categories: spectacular, hard, dark green and pink banded, high-grade metamorphic rocks called *amphibolite gneisses* (2), formed deep in the crust of the Earth; and grey-brown, hard *sandstones*. The gneisses make up the southern half of the peninsula, including the hill of Beinn

2 An igeous dyke cuts ancient amphibolite gneisses on the shore near Bruichladdich.

Tart a' Mhill, and are well exposed on the west coast and on the beach in front of the distillery at **Bruichladdich** (1). The sandstones occupy the lower boggier ground in the north of the area, and the island of Colonsay which is to the north of Islay.

The distillery at Bruichladdich lies opposite Bowmore on the west side of Loch Indaal. Water for the distillery drains from the low boggy hills near the boundary between the sandstone and the gneisses, and is collected in a shallow dam above the distillery from where it is piped (4).

It is regrettable that Bruichladdich was mothballed in 1995 as it is a most significant distillery, not just because of the quality and distinctiveness of its product but because it is the most westerly distillery

*O*ld and *E*xotic

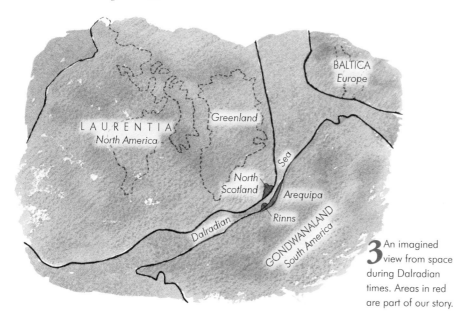

3 An imagined view from space during Dalradian times. Areas in red are part of our story.

(the present South America and Africa) and *Baltica,* separated by the Dalradian sea. The gneisses of Lewis were part of Laurentia, whilst it has been suggested that those of the Rinns were part of the Arequipa coast of present-day South America. The continents moved apart to form the *Iapetus Ocean,* isolating the Rinns from Gondwana, before crashing together in the *Caledonian Orogeny.* They have since split again to form the Atlantic Ocean, isolating Lewis from Greenland.

So the Rinns gneisses have travelled for a thousand million years to provide an exotic whisky in terms of taste and geological romance; and their journey will continue for a thousand million more.

in Scotland and its process water percolates the oldest rocks. The real significance of these Rinns rocks is in the problems they pose to those who wish to interpret their geological position and relationships.

The Dalradian rocks are very old, but the contorted gneisses of Scotland are even older. The Dalradian sea, in which the Bunnahabhain stromatolites flourished and the Port Askaig icebergs melted, lapped around these older rocks.

Once it was thought that all the old gneisses of Scotland were the same age, but now it is clear that the Rinns gneisses are younger (1800 million years) and chemically different to those of the Isle of Lewis and NW Scotland (2800 million years).

These two areas of ancient gneisses are separated by a major fault which runs across Scotland from the northeast to the southwest, from the Moray Firth to Donegal. This is called the Great Glen Fault and along it lie the dark waters of Loch Ness. It is one of the most significant fractures in Scotland.

If we go back to Dalradian times and look down on the Earth from space (3) we see three great continents: *Laurentia* (the present North America and Greenland), *Gondwana*

4 The Bruichladdich water at the take-off point below the dam.

17

The Argyll Islands

The best way to appreciate the whiskies and their waters is to visit the distilleries and their water sources.

For an excellent overview one could do no better than make a strenuous, though not difficult, climb to the summit of Dubh Bheinn on the south of Jura, from the top of which on a clear day you can see almost the whole of both islands. The hill is best approached from Craighouse or the road just to the south. It is possible however to climb more or less direct from the Feolin Ferry landing.

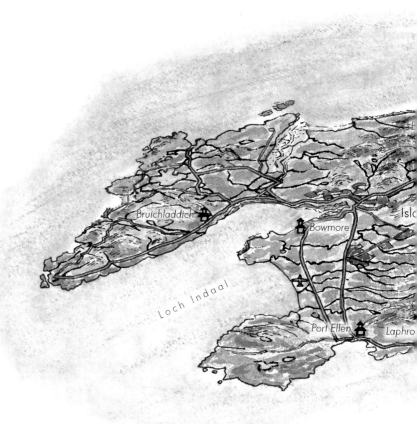

1 The greenstone cross in Kilchoman churchyard is a fine example of Celtic art.

2 Lagavulin Bay from the southwest. The Lagavulin distillery, on the left, sits under a greenstone ridge. In the centre are the lower-lying phyllites and to the right Dunyveg Castle, a stronghold of the Lords of the Isles.

An Argyll Islands Panorama

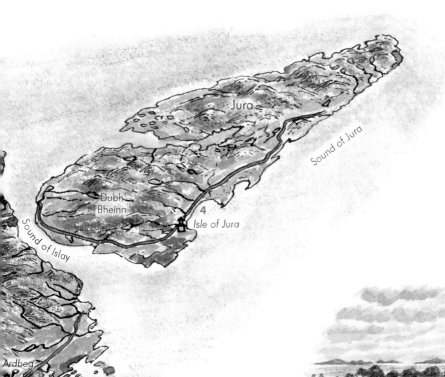

From the summit cairn, Loch Indaal and the Rinns can be seen far to the west. The white buildings of **Bowmore** stand out across the Loch from **Bruichladdich**; closer, **Caol Ila** and **Bunnahabhain** lie across the Sound of Islay with both water sources clearly visible. Below Dubh Bheinn to the south and tucked into the hillside is the Market Loch, source for the Jura distillery itself, whilst away to the southwest are the coastal distilleries of south Islay. On a particularly good day the Mull of Kintyre rises from the sea, and the Antrim coast around **Bushmills** is clearly visible. We shall return to these locations later.

4 Small Isles Bay, Jura, covers eroded phyllites, whilst the islands are formed of the harder greenstones.

3 Quartz House, built entirely of Dalradian quartzite.

Many of the water sources can be seen during very pleasant rambles, ranging from a short walk from the main road above Caol Ila to the *full Bowmore*, a 20 kilometre walk coast to coast across Islay that is a must for the more energetic whisky devotee!

The Grampian Highlands

Location map of the Grampian Highlands.

BGS enhanced satellite image.

1 Winter infrared satellite image of the NE Grampians. The false colours show snow as red, conifer forests as brown, bare fields as blue, and water as black. Some locations referred to in the text are indicated. For some readers, turning the picture upside down may give a better appreciation of the relief.

In the microcosm that is the Argyll Islands we saw hints of a great complexity of geological structure and were introduced to a wide variation in whisky type. But this is nothing in comparison to what we will see by the time our journey through the Grampian Highlands ends on the northeast coast of the Scottish mainland.

A glance at the satellite image (1) shows that the same general NE–SW, *Caledonian* trend that was so plain on Islay and Jura, is also apparent on the mainland, and indeed continues right across the area from coast to coast.

The Grampian Mountains are bordered by two huge faults; one to the northwest, running from Colonsay and Mull to beyond Inverness known as the Great

Glen Fault; the other to the south, the Highland Boundary Fault, running from the Clyde estuary to the coast south of Aberdeen. The actual position of these enormous breaks in the Earth's surface can clearly be seen on satellite images *(see page 52)*. The Great Glen Fault, Scotland's greatest fracture, takes its name from the valley which stretches all the way from Fort William to Inverness. In Gaelic the valley is known as Glen Albyn or Glen Mhor, the latter translating directly as The Great Glen. **Glen Albyn** and **Glen Mhor** were the names given to two malt whiskies distilled in Inverness using the soft, peaty waters of Loch Ness. Both distilleries closed in the 1980s and neither is in existence today.

Between these great faults are the Grampian Highlands, the result of a great collision. It all began around 750 million years ago when what is now the northern part of Scotland together with North America became separated from South America and Europe by the Dalradian sea *(page 17)*. In this sea were deposited sandstones, mudstones and limestones which were to become the rocks we now call the Dalradian. Over the succeeding 200 million years the two great continental masses moved apart to form the Iapetus Ocean before coming together again to squeeze and squash the rocks during the Caledonian Orogeny (2). The heat and pressure generated by

this process changed or metamorphosed most of these rocks and melted others to form granites and lava flows. The collision produced a great mountain range, like the present Himalayas, but 400 million years of weathering has stripped away kilometres of rock so that today we see rocks that were formed at great depths.

The Grampian Highlands are the result of this great collision, and within the hills and mountains, the gentle valleys and deep glens, lie the water sources of over 50 distilleries, including, in the far northeast, a great concentration around the valley of the River Spey.

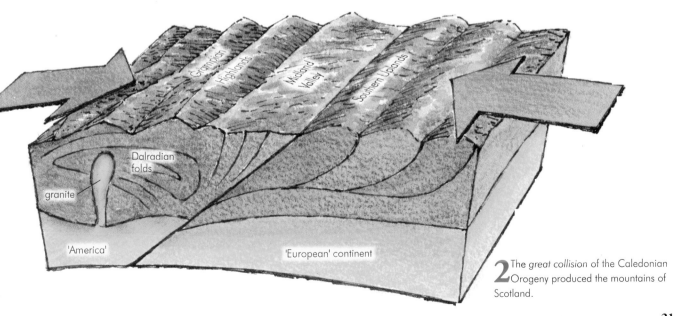

2 The *great collision* of the Caledonian Orogeny produced the mountains of Scotland.

The Grampian Highlands

'He who first met the Highlands' swelling blue
Would love each peak that shows a kindred hue.'
Lord Byron, *The Island*.

The collision forces were from the northwest and southeast producing the NE–SW Caledonian alignment of folded rocks and faults, and establishing the geological pattern of the Grampian Highlands (1)

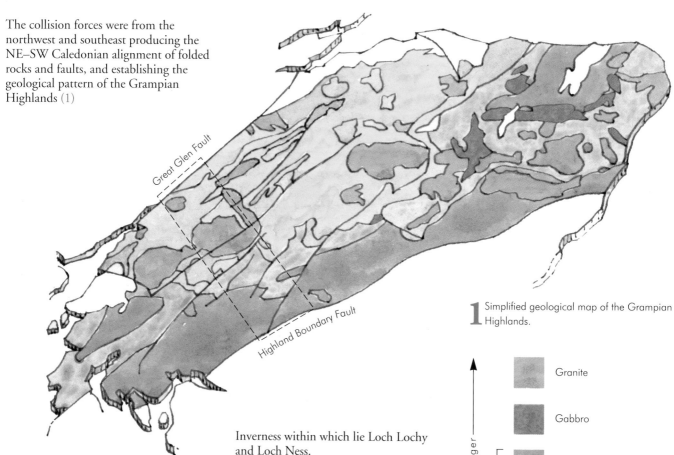

1 Simplified geological map of the Grampian Highlands.

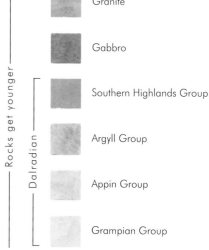

Granite

Gabbro

Southern Highlands Group

Argyll Group

Appin Group

Grampian Group

Rocks get younger →

Dalradian

The Great Glen Fault is a belt of torn and smashed rocks produced by the sides of the fault moving horizontally in opposite directions. Because these smashed rocks are easier to weather, the fault is now marked by the deep sea loch of Loch Linnhe and the steep-sided valley stretching from Fort William to

Inverness within which lie Loch Lochy and Loch Ness.

In contrast, the line of the Highland Boundary Fault in the south has a different though no less dramatic physical presence. Unlike the Great Glen Fault, the land on either side of the Highland Boundary Fault moved vertically, so forming an outstanding feature which, as the name suggests, separates the older mountains to the north from the broad fertile plains of

1 & 2 The rocks of the Grampian Highlands have been divided into four Dalradian groups, the colours for which apply to both illustrations. We have tried to show the Tay Nappe structure *(right)*, much of which was originally above the present land surface.

2 Schematic block section of the Grampian Highlands cut from the position indicated on the map opposite (1)

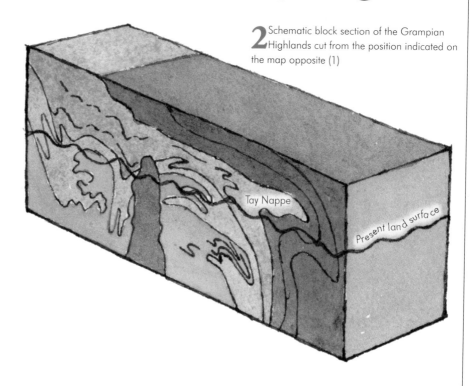

Tay Nappe

Present land surface

the Midland Valley to the south. Drive north from the Clyde estuary or look north from the motorway (M9) as it passes Stirling and you will see the mountains suddenly rise from the plain.

Incredibly, even today, movements along these faults still occur, though fortunately now on a very small scale. This is only to be expected from features so dramatic that they stand out clearly when seen from space *(see page 52)*.

The general NE–SW trend of the Grampian mountains between these faults belies the great complexities into which the rocks have been folded and faulted. A key feature on Islay and Jura was the anticline tilted to the northwest. But this is only a local structure. Most of the mainland rocks were squeezed into a huge mushroom-shaped mass which slowly flowed to the southeast to form the great *Tay Nappe* (2). This was refolded again and again, and at times had hot, molten, granite magma intruded into it. Volcanic vents poured lava out over it during later stages in its development.

The combination of compression and heating at great depth in the Earth's

crust to temperatures above 450°C caused the mineral transformations called metamorphism which dramatically changed the appearance of the rocks: sandstones became quartzites; muds, phyllites or *schists*; and limestones, *marbles*.

It has taken many decades of painstaking study and analysis before this interpretation of the geology of the Grampians was reached and generally accepted. Fortunately, many of the rocks are distinctive, and can be identified and mapped right across the whole region; for

example, remember the Port Askaig Tillite? This particular rock, known locally by different names *(Baravulin Boulder Bed, Schiehallion Boulder Bed, Sron na Gaoithe Boulder Bed)*, can be found throughout the Grampians and used as a marker to sort out the nature of the great folds and contortions.

Here truly is the coming together of the immensity of Scottish geology with the complexity of a myriad of distillates. In these great mountains the forces of Nature and the juice of the barley become kindred spirits.

The Grampian Highlands

The geological map on page 22 shows us that the contorted rocks of the Grampians generally become older as we journey northwards and an excellent way to appreciate this change is to travel by road (A9) from Perth to Inverness *(see page 20)*. The delights of this *geotraverse* are enhanced by sampling six superb malts along the way.

Heading north from Perth (1) across the flat, fertile red sandstone plains with the mountains misty blue in the distance, we strike the west bank of the River Tay. Suddenly, we notice the land has changed, and just before Dunkeld we cross the Highland Boundary Fault and enter the Highlands.

Eight miles on we reach Ballinluig where the rivers Tay and Tummel meet. We will follow the Tay first and turn west along the A827 for a 16 kilometre drive to **Aberfeldy**. At the eastern end of this spa town is a distillery fed by the north-flowing Pittiely Burn, which tumbles down the grassy hillsides of grey *grits*, greenstones and sandstones. These rocks are the youngest and least-metamorphosed Dalradian we shall see.

The spirit is fresh, crisp and slightly peaty and well worth the diversion.

Returning to Ballinluig we continue our northerly progression to Pitlochry. Here are two distilleries, very different in characteristics and drawing their process waters from different sources. **Edradour** (2), the smallest distillery in Scotland, lies a couple of kilometres east of the town and takes its water from the Edradour Burn which drains the peat

1 The A9 road from Perth to Dalwhinnie.

2 Edradour distillery, the smallest in Scotland.

24

(Of Perthshire) *'In this district is to be found everything requisite for establishing a natural history.'* J Hutton, *Theory of the Earth, 1795.*

3 Ben Vrackie, the source for the Blair Atholl Distillery, viewed from just east of Pitlochry.

ie

Atholl Distillery
⌂ *Edradour*

BALLINLUIG

River Tummel

Highland Boundary Fault

PERTH

bogs to the northeast. These bogs overlie sandstones of similar type and age to those at Aberfeldy; the *Ben Ledi Grits*. The whisky too is similar, being light, golden and gently smoky.

Situated right in the middle of Pitlochry is the **Blair Atholl** distillery, a series of pleasant stone buildings clustered around a burn. This stream is not the process water — that comes from five kilometres to the north from Loch a' Choire in a col high up on the heathery, southern slopes of Ben Vrackie (3). We have progressed down the succession now and are in

slates, graphitic schists and greenstones similar to, and of the same age as, those we last saw along the southeast coast of Islay. This sweet spirity whisky is the successor of the stuff reputed to have put fire into the bellies of the Highlanders as they swept south to victory through the Pass of Killiecrankie in 1689.

On leaving Pitlochry we rejoin the main road and continue north through the narrow gorge of the River Garry at Killiecrankie and, after passing the village of Blair Atholl, start the long climb that leads to our next destination.

25

The Grampian Highlands

Just after the village of Blair Atholl, the slates, phyllites and limestones disappear, and from now on we see only monotonous grey, stripy, impure quartzites. These are the *Grampian Group*, the oldest of the Dalradian rocks. On the acid soils, few trees, other than conifer plantations, break the heather moorland.

1 The A9 road from Dalwhinne to Inverness.

Lochan na Doire-uaine, a crystal-clear, snow-fed lake high up in the hills to the west.

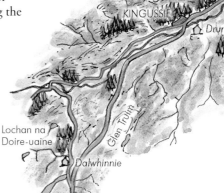

2 Dalwhinnie, the highest distillery in Scotland, in winter garb.

After climbing through Glen Garry, the road turns north again and continues to rise through the Pass of Drumochter. Suddenly at the top, in the midst of a desolate wide bowl surrounded by deeply eroded mountains, we see for the first time **Dalwhinnie** distillery (2), the highest in Scotland at 350 metres above sea level. Totally encompassed by extensive peat deposits, it sits in splendid isolation amongst the mounds of glacial morainic material. Its water comes from

Having paused to sample this wild, aromatic, peaty distillate we start to descend Glen Truim into the valley of the youthful River Spey (1). Crossing the river at Kingussie, we look eastwards beyond the eerie ruins of Ruthven Barracks and spy a distillery that has only recently started producing a malt in its own right. The Speyside distillery is at Tromie Mills on the east bank of the Tromie River which is its water source. The spirity, dry, earthy whisky that it produces, **Drumguish,** is a welcome addition to the malts of the Highlands.

26

'Malt whisky holds within it the climates and characters of Scotland — each one is a distillation of its locality.' Trevor Cowan.

Continuing, we see the high granite mountains of Cairn Gorm to the right and the even more desolate Monadhliath mountain range on our left. At Aviemore we leave the valley of the Spey and after Carrbridge start to climb once again, passing the summit most appropriately named for our journey, *Slochd!* Then down into the valley of the Findhorn and, where the road and railway cross the river, lies **Tomatin**. Here is yet another superlative on this journey: the largest malt whisky distillery in Scotland. With 23 stills and a capacity of five million litres of proof spirit per year, the distillery itself looks like a large factory, but the walk to the water source and the take off point is a tremendous experience.

Come here in the early spring, when the snow has not yet melted from the juniper bushes and silver birches that crowd into the lower parts of the valley of the Allt na Frith (3). The source of this very special stream is on the lonely peat-covered quartzite hills of Carn Dubh and Beinn Bhreac. We are now at the very bottom of the Dalradian succession in an area which experienced the very high temperatures and pressures deep in the Earth's crust; so high that the rocks have started to melt in places. These melted rocks are called *migmatites*

3 The juniper-filled valley of the Allt na Frith in winter looking towards Tomatin distillery.

and we are in the *Central Highland Migmatite Complex*.

We shall see no more distilleries today, but to complete our geological journey we continue north on the A9 to Inverness. Just after Daviot the road drops steeply onto the red sandstone plains that we will see again in the next chapter. Cross the bridge over the Beauly Firth at Inverness and you have crossed the Great Glen Fault!

A sprig of Juniper.

27

The Grampian Highlands

1 Knock Hill from the east. The piles of gabbro boulders have been cleared from the ploughed fields.

At a breathless pace we have completed a journey from south to north across the whole of the Grampian Highlands and have seen great changes in the rocks. We will now look at another important ingredient of Grampian geology.

Before, during and after the Caledonian Orogeny, hot, molten material or *magma* from deep in the Earth was squeezed up into the rocks where it crystallised; some even broke through to the surface as volcanoes, pouring out ash and lava flows.

Seven phases of such magmatism have been identified, each with its own characteristics, but we need only concern ourselves with four. The study of these will take us from dark green gabbros amongst the rolling hills and pastoral farmlands of the northeast, through the high mountains of the centre and west, formed from red and pink granites, to dark lavas on the western seaboard near Oban.

On the Moray Firth coast of Banffshire lies the fishing port of Portsoy, famous itself throughout the world for its cliffs of dark green and red serpentine; a rock that for many years has been locally polished and carved into ornaments and sold as *Portsoy marble*. The term is geologically a misnomer for in reality it is a metamorphosed igneous rock.

South of Portsoy, in Banff and northern Aberdeenshire, large volumes of very hot, iron- and magnesium-rich magmas from the Earth's depths crystallised around 470 million years ago during the folding of the Dalradian rocks.

In an area east of Keith and stretching from south of Huntly to the north coast, several of these intrusions formed large masses. The magma cooled at great depths to form the coarse-grained, dark rock called *gabbro*. Although the rock covers a large area, it weathers easily and does not form many natural rocky features. Fortunately its study has been helped by man to such an extent that the great geologist, H H Read, once

Valves of burnished copper adorn the stills.

Water emerges in a series of springs in the wooded lower slopes marking the boundary between the gabbro and the overlying Dalradian schists. The springs provide water for the small village of Knock, and the distillery, originally called **Knockdhu**, now sells its fresh, sweet and light malt whisky as **An Cnoc**.

Gabbro lies beneath the level farmland around the distillery itself, and whilst it cannot be seen in place, look for it in the walls surrounding the fields and the huge piles of boulders that have been cleared into the field corners.

2 Samples of the Insch Gabbro from the British Geological Survey collection, Edinburgh.

remarked that *'gabbros are always found in railway cuttings'*.

To the determined whisky devotee two of these gabbro masses are of particular interest. Firstly, there is one which stretches for 12 kilometres south from near Portsoy. This forms the base of Knock Hill (1), a distinctive feature visible for great distances rising to 430 metres above the surrounding plains.

Further to the south is the largest and most well known of the masses, the *Insch Gabbro* (2). Near its western boundary this is cut by the pink or pale *Kennethmont Granite* which forms Knockandy Hill (3) From this hill, 17 springs are reputed to provide the pure soft process waters for **Ardmore**, a rarely bottled, remarkably dry and earthily distinct malt.

Even after the intensive folding of the Dalradian rocks had ended, huge volumes

of granitic magmas rose up into the metamorphosed sediments. We have already seen one of the biggest from the A9: the Cairngorms — beautiful mountains, but a desert for our purposes, as not a single distillery takes its water from them.

3 Knockandy Hill: a granite hill on which it is reputed that 17 springs provide the process waters for Ardmore distillery (left).

The Grampian Highlands

However, a few miles to the east of the Cairngorms there is another large *granite* mountain described by Byron as *'the steep frowning glories of dark Lochnagar'*. This mountain which dominates the castle of Balmoral is also the source of water for the adjacent **Royal Lochnagar** distillery. The sweet, clear, heathery stream contributes to a distillate of similar nature: for 150 years a royal favourite. Did the young Queen Victoria and her consort sit awhile, as we should, by the upper dam (1) and watch the dragonflies at noon in deep summer?

Be sure to look at the large blocks which have been used to build the Reception Centre (2) and you will appreciate the

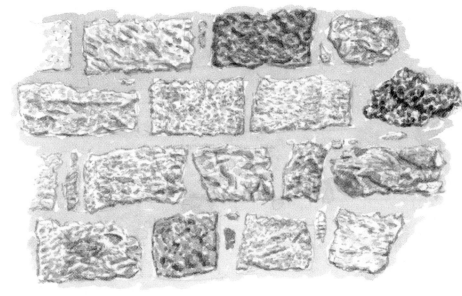

2 The wall of the Visitor Centre at Royal Lochnagar showing a wide variety of local granites and other rocks.

variety of *igneous* rocks present in this part of Scotland.

But there is another of these huge granite masses that provides water for a distillery and to see it we must return to the west coast, to the edge of the Great Glen on the southern shore of Loch Linnhe. Towering above the town of Fort William is the highest *ben* of all, the mighty Ben Nevis. Below the dark brooding corries of the northern face, with their permanent snow, the Mill Burn (*Allt a Mhuilinn*) rises at Buchan's Well. From a source at over 1200 metres, the water, described as having a strange bluish tinge, rushes down towards

1 The upper dam at Royal Lochnagar.

'Read me a lesson, muse, and speak it loud
Upon the top of Nevis blind in Mist!'
John Keats, *On Ben Nevis.*

the **Ben Nevis** distillery (3) where it is transformed into a deep amber-coloured liquid with a dry, spi, spicy flavour.

Ben Nevis is essentially the root of an ancient volcano, and there are still lava flows preserved on top of the mountain where they form the dark crags of the northern face.

To see such volcanic rocks more easily, it is better to travel southwest to **Oban**, a popular fishing port and tourist centre, sheltered from the southwesterly winds by the island of Kerrera. Here, the whole of the Lorn plateau is made up of these lavas which were extruded during late Silurian/early Devonian times. The town reservoir, Loch Gleann a Bhearraidh, sits

on the volcanic rocks and provides the water for the sweet, smoky smooth liquid created at the distillery on the sea front.

There is one other large granite mass we must look at in the Grampians, and to do that we must return to the northeast and enter the wide valleys and rolling hills of the River Spey and its tributaries.

3 Allt a Mhuilinn and Ben Nevis, the roots of a great volcano, in winter garb.

Ben Nevis

Ben Nevis distillery

Allt a Mhuilinn

The Grampian Highlands

The River Spey rises high in the granite Monadhliath mountains, southeast of the Great Glen and flows east and northeastwards for over 120 kilometres to reach the North Sea between Lossiemouth and Buckie. It is one of the great rivers of Scotland, famous for its beauty and its salmon fishing, and synonymous throughout the world with whiskies of quality.

We have already seen the young river sparkling through the glacial moraines as we drove along the A9. Beyond Dalwhinnie and as far as Aviemore, where we turned north, road, rail and river run together.

In whisky terms, Speyside refers to an area surrounding the lower Spey valley from Grantown on Spey in the southwest to Fochabers in the northeast. The area also includes the valleys of the River Avon, which lies to the east and flows north to join the Spey at Cragganmore, and its tributary the Livet. Further north, the Fiddich and the Dullan, which come together at Dufftown, flow into the Spey at Craigellachie. The distilleries in and around the town of Keith, even further east, which stands on the River Isla, are also usually included.

This is big country, where the barley fields of the wide, fertile, alluvium-filled valleys contrast with the bare or wooded slopes of the rolling hills; and in every valley is a broad, dark, gently flowing river with green-booted fishermen along the banks. In this area there are over 30 distilleries, each one producing an individual and characteristic 'nectar'.

The general NE–SW grain of the topography is yet another reflection of the Caledonian trend we have been observing since we visited the Argyll Islands and it is along this trend we shall travel to visit each one of the distilleries.

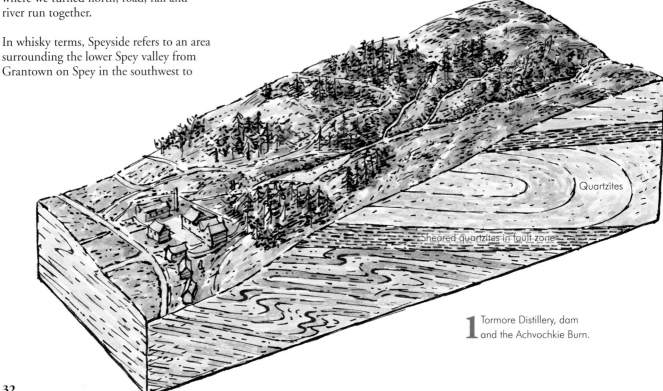

Quartzites

Sheared quartzites in fault zone

1 Tormore Distillery, dam and the Achvochkie Burn.

32

You may follow this route on pages 36–37.

*B*eside the *S*pey

There is nothing here in the geology that we have not experienced already in the last few pages, it is just that in this small area the different rock groups come together. To the north and the west the region is made up of the oldest of Dalradian rocks: the Grampian Group. There is little variety in these rocks and most of the succession is made up of white or grey quartzites. To the east and the south are the younger, more variable Dalradian rocks. Here there are limestones and schists mixed in with the quartzites. And right in the middle, forming Ben Rinnes and the Conval Hills, is a granite mass similar to those we have seen in earlier pages.

The journey starts just north of Grantown on the eastern banks of the Spey itself. The main road (A95), which winds northeastwards with the river, runs through a wide wooded valley with bare hills to right and left. Just south of the village of Cromdale, we see on the right the chimney of the mothballed **Balmenach** distillery. It was the most westerly of all the Speyside distilleries and took its water from the Hills of Cromdale to the south. These bleak, heather-covered slopes are underlain by the clean, crystalline quartzites of the Grampian Group.

The best opportunity to see these rocks is further along the road at the distillery of **Tormore** (1). A walk behind the distillery past the dam takes you into a mystical fairy glen of grass, wild flowers and fir trees, and at the far end, where the white quartzites form a cliff, the process water flows from joints in the rocks, eventually to come together as the Achvochkie Burn. Above the cliffs the lower slopes of the hill of Craggan More stretch upwards. Stand by the dam, glass in hand, with the fragrant pale spirit diluted with the water from the burn and you are one step from heaven!

Further along the road we pass the **Cragganmore** distillery on the left. This takes its water from the Craggan Burn, another stream on the hill after which the distillery is named. Then in and out of the valley of the Avon until, as the **Glenfarclas** distillery appears to our right, we cross the Spey to the western bank and enter the village of **Cardhu**. There is a distillery here, taking waters from the quartzites of Carn na Cailliche to the north, and down by the riverside two more. One of these, **Knockando**, draws its process waters from the Cardnach Spring above the distillery. The waters here come originally from the same hills to the north.

The other, **Tamdhu** (2), is unique in that it uses waters from a well in the river gravels directly under the distillery and is in fact the only distillery in the whole of Speyside actually to utilise water from the Spey itself for making whisky. On any visit you should try this dry, light spirit and then make comparison with the slightly sweeter, gently peaty products from the previous two distilleries: Cardhu, a fine amber colour, and Knockando, the palest of all yellows.

2 At Tamdhu there is a well into the River Spey gravels right under the distillery. The section is drawn from top left to bottom right.

The Grampian Highlands

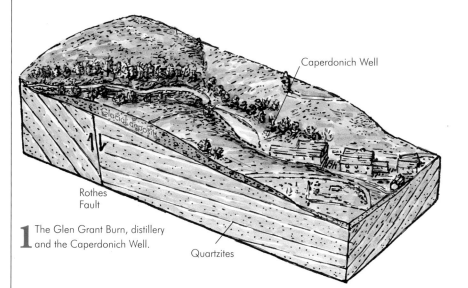

1 The Glen Grant Burn, distillery and the Caperdonich Well.

Hills beyond spring the process waters for more than a dozen distilleries.

Having regained the A95, our journey northwards continues. High on the granite mountain flanks we see the **Ben Rinnes** distillery, and further north **Glenallachie,** and then on to the dour stone village of Charlestown of Aberlour. In the Celtic past St Drostan baptised his converts with water from a spring near here. Now this same 'granite' water is itself converted into a no-less-divine spirit; the light, spirity, sweet **Aberlour**.

On we go, until, on the other river bank we pass sweet **Macallan**, matured only in *Oloroso* barrels; and then north on the

The same road that brought us to the village of Cardhu takes us east for another mile before we turn south towards the Spey, the village of Carron and the **Imperial** distillery. Over the bridge, around a bend and suddenly before us is dark, smoky **Dailuaine**. Deep in the wooded valley it is always cool, even in midsummer, and this dankness, together with the granite waters of the Bailliemullich Burn from the lower slopes of Ben Rinnes, contribute to this amber, full bodied, smooth whisky.

We shake free from the all-enveloping valley and mount the cliffs on the other bank of the river and instantly there it is, just to the right, much closer now, the great, bare, rounded mountain of Ben Rinnes with the angular rocky *scurrans* marking its summit. From these glaciated granite slopes and those of the Conval

2 Glacial sands on the lower slopes of Meikle Conval, south of Dufftown.

34

You may follow this route on pages 36–37.

Central Speyside

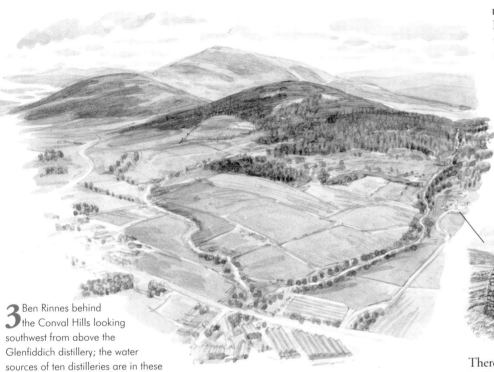

3 Ben Rinnes behind the Conval Hills looking southwest from above the Glenfiddich distillery; the water sources of ten distilleries are in these hills. *Inset shows the Robbie Dubh spring.*

taking waters from the north-flowing Bardon Burn. Within the complex three malts are produced: sweet **Glenlossie**, pale **Mannochmore** and the famous black malt, **Lochdhu**.

Returning through Rothes we cross the A95 and at **Craigellachie** we return to granite sources. Continuing south down the Fiddich Valley towards Dufftown we pass first **Balvenie** (now closed) and then the famous **Glenfiddich** (3), which takes its waters from the Robbie Dubh, a spring on the lower slopes of Little Conval. At the site of the spring there is a large stone cairn *(left)*.

There are four other working distilleries in Dufftown, said to have been built on *seven stills*. Down in the Fiddich valley is **Glendullan** taking water from higher up the river, and then round the corner on Dullan Water are **Mortlach** and **Dufftown-Pittyvaich** both of which tap springs in the glacial sands on the slopes of Meikle Conval (2).

To complete the circuit of the Ben Rinnes granite we must take the Tomintoul road (B9009) south from Dufftown for six kilometres to pass the new distillery of **Allt A'Bhainne** and spy high on the hillside, the fenced area marking its water source.

A941 to Rothes; second only to Dufftown in the number of distilleries within its boundaries: **Glen Spey** and **Glenrothes** to the south, light aromatic **Speyburn** to the north and in between, facing each other across the road in the centre of the village, **Caperdonich** to the east and the mighty **Glen Grant** to the west. Water sources for these two are the Glen Grant Burn which, like the other Rothes distilleries, drains water from the quartzite hills to the west; and the Caperdonich Well (1) in the river gravels

below the Glen Grant dam. These waters are probably blended to add to the mysteries of the spirits.

The valley to the north of Rothes follows the large Rothes Fault which separates the Grampian Group quartzites to the west from the Old Red Sandstones to the east. Most of the distilleries on the road will be mentioned in the next chapter but we should mention now the large distillery complex to the northwest. This is very definitely a Grampian Group distillery

The Grampian Highlands — A Speyside Panorama

The Speyside distilleries tap their waters from the contorted and folded Dalradian rocks and the granites of Ben Rinnes and Glenlivet. We have cut through the landscape to show the distilleries in their geological setting.

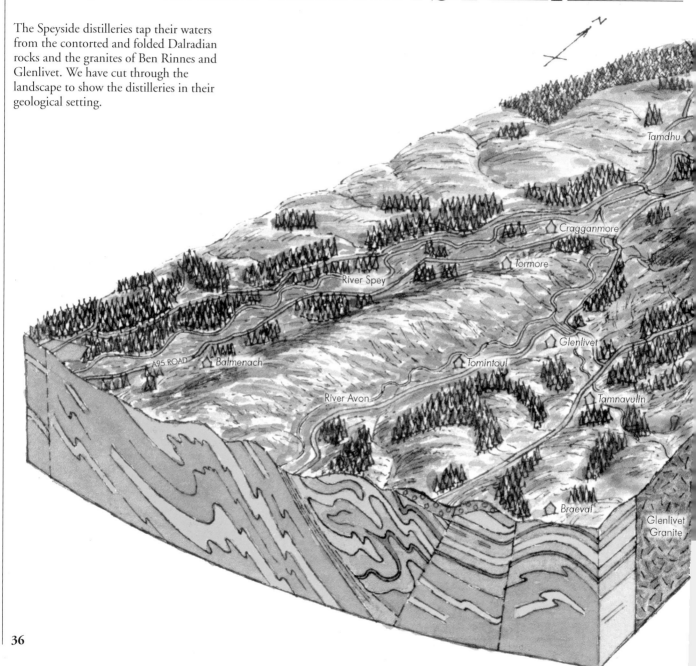

Tamdhu

Cragganmore

Tormore

River Spey

Glenlivet

A95 ROAD   Balmenach

Tomintoul

Tamnavulin

River Avon

Braeval

Glenlivet Granite

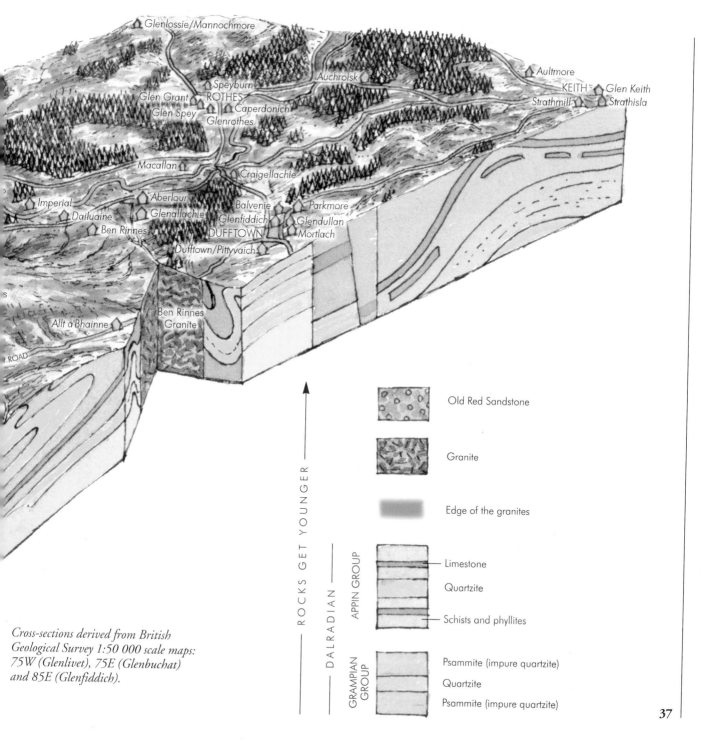

Glenlossie/Mannochmore

Aultmore

KEITH

Glen Keith

Strathmill

Strathisla

Speyburn

Auchroisk

Glen Grant

ROTHES

Caperdonich

Glen Spey

Glenrothes

Macallan

Craigellachie

Imperial

Aberlour

Balvenie

Parkmore

Dailuaine

Glenallachie

Glenfiddich

Glendullan

Ben Rinnes

DUFFTOWN

Mortlach

Dufftown/Pittyvaich

Allt a'Bhainne

Ben Rinnes
Granite

ROAD

*Cross-sections derived from British
Geological Survey 1:50 000 scale maps:
75W (Glenlivet), 75E (Glenbuchat)
and 85E (Glenfiddich).*

ROCKS GET YOUNGER

DALRADIAN

APPIN GROUP

GRAMPIAN GROUP

Old Red Sandstone

Granite

Edge of the granites

Limestone

Quartzite

Schists and phyllites

Psammite (impure quartzite)

Quartzite

Psammite (impure quartzite)

37

The Grampian Highlands

'For men of sense must own tis better
To drink good malt than starve on water.'
Anon.

1 Glenlivet Distillery, with Josie's Well in the foreground.

Twenty-seven down and 11 to go! Speyside has *whisky galore!*

A few miles beyond Allt A'Bhainne on the B9009 we see in front of us perhaps the most famous of all malt distilleries, certainly the one whose very name conjures up Speyside whiskies: **Glenlivet** (1). Indeed, not so very long ago, so many distilleries attached this name to their own that Glen Livet was described as *'the longest glen in the world'*. This rich, dry, golden spirit is created using water taken from Josie's Well, a local spring in the glacial gravels and sands in the fields behind the distillery.

From Glenlivet we can turn either southwest or due south. To the southwest

is Strath Avon and the **Tomintoul** distillery drawing its waters from the Ballantruan Spring on the quartzite slopes of Cairn Ballantruan which dominates the buildings. To the south of Glenlivet is the mothballed **Tamnavulin**, and even further south, hiding amongst the backroads around Chapeltown, is **Braes of Glenlivet** now renamed as the bronze-coloured, sweet distillate, **Braeval.**

It is a long way to retrace our steps to Craigellachie, but that is where we must go next, then north to Mulben and then east towards Keith. Just after Mulben are the futuristic buildings of the new Auchroisk distillery, opened in 1975,

2 Strathisla Distillery and the Fairy Well: a haunting taste.

You may follow this route on pages 36–37.

Speyside — Keith and Beyond

producing the light and golden **Singleton of Auchroisk**. In the cliffs on the side of a secret glen below the buildings is a spring called Dorie's Well (3). From here the water is pumped to tanks above the distillery to give sufficient head of water. Lucky visitors may get the chance to stand in the stone shelter that hides the spring and dilute their dram at its source.

And so to Keith, another distillery town, this time built almost entirely of granite from a single quarry. Three distilleries cluster around the River Isla as it winds its way through the town. Pale, sweet **Strathmill** to the south with a borehole into the river gravels, then amber **Glen Keith** to the north and almost opposite the light and spicy **Strathisla**. The water for Strathisla is collected in the hills and stored in a reservoir, the Fairy Well, next to the distillery. Whatever the chemical composition, it is held that the particular characteristics of these waters are due to nightly visitations by *fays and fairies* who haunt the well (2). Who are we to say?

3 Dorie's Well in a secret glen near Auchroisk.

The fourth of the Keith distilleries is north on the old Portgordon road (B9106) where **Aultmore** stands, taking spring waters from the fields around Auchinderran. Then the hills die away, the coastal plain is before us. On the coast to the northeast, in the far distance, is Banff and the **Macduff** distillery, usually sold as **Glen Deveron**.

To the south-east, beyond Huntly, is **Glendronach**, almost the last of the Grampian distilleries. Due north, below us, on the coastal plain near to the town of Buckie is **Inchgower**. Situated on the fertile red soils of the *Old Red Sandstone* its waters come from the inland hills. A small track opposite the distillery leads up a gentle slope to the dam (4) and from here we look north and reflect upon the wonders we have seen and on what our next adventure will reveal.

4 Buckie and the North Sea looking northwards from the Inchgower Dam.

The Far North

'Farewell to the Highlands, farewell to the North,
The birth-place of Valour, the country of Worth.'
Robert Burns, *My Heart's in the Highlands.*

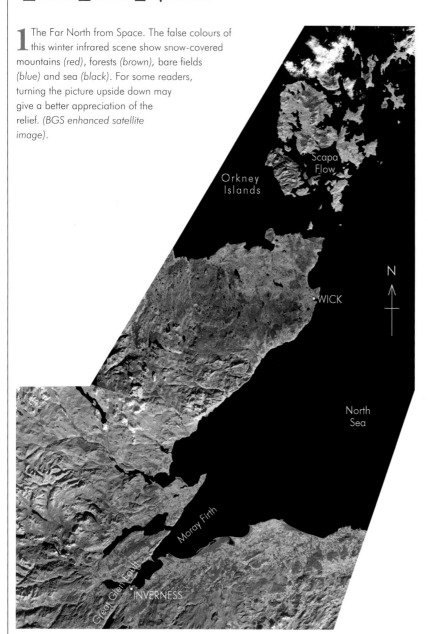

1 The Far North from Space. The false colours of this winter infrared scene show snow-covered mountains *(red)*, forests *(brown)*, bare fields *(blue)* and sea *(black)*. For some readers, turning the picture upside down may give a better appreciation of the relief. *(BGS enhanced satellite image).*

Orkney Islands

Scapa Flow

WICK

North Sea

Moray Firth

Great Glen Fault

INVERNESS

Location map of the Far North.

Our tour of the distilleries of the Grampians ended with us standing by the dam on the hill of Millbuie looking northwestwards over the distillery of Inchgower and the town of Buckie.

The view from here on a good day — and there are many good days up here — is stunning and allows us to identify all but the northern extremities of our next journey.

Below us the shallow hills fall away to the red, sandy-soiled, fertile plains of the Laich o' Moray, often wooded on the more sandy parts, but renowned for the quality and quantity of the barley that is grown to supply the ever-rapacious distilleries inland.

Beyond the coastal strip, which stretches westwards into the distance, lie the chill blue waters of the North Sea. In the far distance, getting progressively further away from left to right we see the coastline of Sutherland with the smoky-grey hills behind. Further north but out of sight lie the flat lands of Caithness and the islands of Orkney.

We are in effect standing on the southern margin of a *marine basin* into which mud and sand is being carried by rivers flowing into the North Sea from the mountains to the south and the west (1). Those to the south are carved from Dalradian rocks, with which we are familiar; to the north the mountains are formed from the highly metamorphosed and contorted rocks of the *Moinian* (2).

By one of those fascinating geological coincidences, had we been standing on the same spot some 380 million years ago the general situation would have been quite similar. Of course there would not have been any houses, people or animals, or even vegetation on the land, and the climate would have been much hotter and drier; but we would still be looking at a *basin* with high Dalradian mountains (perhaps as high as the present Alps) to the south and the Moinian to the west. The red and brown soils of Moray give us the clue to the contents of this older basin: they are the sediments of the Old Red Sandstone of Devonian age *(see column on page 7)*.

We can, in this case, agree with the approach of Charles Lyell, a founding father of geology, that '*the present is the key to the past*'.

2 Simplified geological map of the Far North.

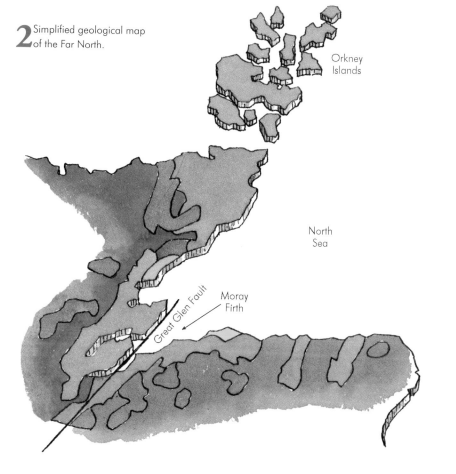

Orkney Islands

North Sea

Great Glen Fault

Moray Firth

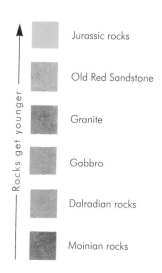

Rocks get younger

Jurassic rocks

Old Red Sandstone

Granite

Gabbro

Dalradian rocks

Moinian rocks

The Far North

'We see the distant gleam of scales'
Hugh Miller, *Old Red Sandstone.*

1 Artist's impression of the Orcadian Basin during Old Red Sandstone times.

Pterichthys

Our journey will take us along the edge of both the present-day basin and the ancient Devonian one, usually called by geologists the Orcadian Basin (1). The southern part of this old basin was a flat, desolate alluvial plain onto which cascaded the jumbled pebbles and fragments of screes and alluvial fans that resulted from the erosion of the surrounding mountains. We see these now as sandstones and *conglomerates*.

To the north, in the area now Caithness and the Orkneys, the situation was different. Here, for much of Devonian times, there was a large shallow lake into which sands and clays were laid down in a rhythmic succession of sandstones and shales as the water levels rose and fell during this time of arid conditions. These gave rise to the flaggy, well-bedded, brown rocks that produce the characteristically flat scenery of the far north, with coastal erosion resulting in the dramatic cliffs of Caithness.

But there was some life here, in fact life so exotic in form that it has inspired many geologists, amongst whom the most famous was the naturalist and stonemason

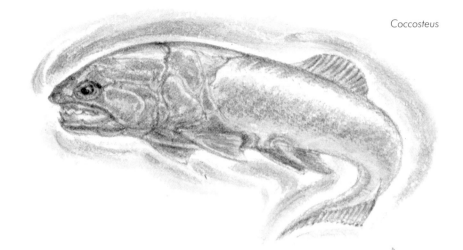

Coccosteus

Hugh Miller (2), born and bred in Cromarty. His studies of the rocks and fossils of the Old Red Sandstone were pioneering classics.

The waters of the Orcadian Lake were teeming with *fish*; not fish as we know them today but strange armoured fish which proliferated during Old Red Sandstone times. The conditions of quiet sedimentation were ideal for *fossilisation*, and the fish beds which occur throughout the succession are world famous and have produced many beautifully preserved whole specimens for museums and collectors.

The waters for some of the northern whiskies have percolated through these sediments and fish remains which remind us of a time when all life on Earth was still aquatic.

2 From a small house in the village of Cromarty, Hugh Miller (1802–1856), stonemason, naturalist and preacher, systematically studied the Old Red Sandstone strata and its fossils, especially the fish, some of which are reconstructed on these pages.

Tristichopterus

The Far North

'Whisky belongs to the alchemist's den and to the long nights shot with cold and flickering beams.' Aeneas MacDonald.

1 The old Prior's lodgings in the grounds of Pluscarden Abbey.
Bottom right: A well in the corner of the walled gardens at Pluscarden.

Where there are calcareous sandstones, there are often mineralised ground waters, and where there is *hard* water, there are often breweries, for the high concentrations of calcium assist in the brewing process. The **Glen Moray** distillery in Elgin was a brewery but currently uses the soft waters of the river Lossie. If recent concerns over low flow rates result in the use of a borehole source, it will be interesting to see what effects more-mineralised water will have on the distillate.

A few miles to the southeast of Elgin, in the peace and solitude of the wooded valley of the Black Burn, lies the site of medieval Scotland's most famous brewery: the Benedictine priory of Pluscarden (1). The early monks used a combination of soft waters from the Black Burn and hard water from wells in the grounds to make an ale which *'made the hearts of all rejoice and filled the abbey with unutterable bliss, raising the devotions to the pitch that the surrounding hills echoed with their hallelujahs'*.

The monks are still there and the traditions are continued at the site of one of the priory's old mills: the distillery of **Miltonduff**, still on the banks of the Black Burn which it utilises for cooling water. Its process waters come from boreholes under the distillery. A glass of this fine amber spirit is a toast of thanks to those ancient clerics.

There have always been a number of distilleries along the coastal plains between Elgin and Nairn, such as

The transition from the rolling, glacially smoothed hills of Speyside is dramatic and obvious just after passing Buckie on the main road to Elgin. We are instantly on flat arable Old Red Sandstone plains. The sweet golden whiskies of **Longmorn, Benriach, Glen Elgin,**

Linkwood and the now-closed **Coleburn** draw their waters from the slopes of the aptly named *Brown Muir*, just north of Rothes, the reddish brown soils of which are underlain by the Devonian sandstones and conglomerates of the Orcadian Basin.

Monks, Malts and Sanctuary

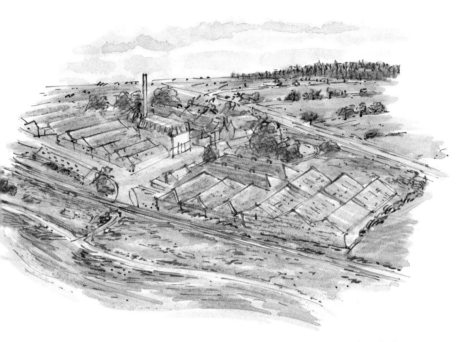

2 Glenmorangie distillery from the sea, with Tarlogie Hill in the background.

The low-lying fertile land and the evidence from red sandstone walls tells us that we are still in Old Red Sandstone country. Indeed we are now approaching a distillery that shouts from the hilltops that it uses hard water and attributes much of the character of its product to this mineralised water: **Glenmorangie** (2). This distillery is another that started off as a brewery. The buildings themselves (4) provide the serious student with an unending series of specimens of the rocks through which the process water flows to bubble up into the rustic fenced dam around the Tarlogie Spring (3). The water itself and stills with the highest necks in Scotland, combine to produce a light, spirity malt with a colour matching the golden gorse of Tarlogie Hill. To this day, any whisky devotee would be happy to seek sanctuary in Tain!

Glenburgie and **Royal Brackla**, which are still operating. Several others have had water supply problems, such as lack of constant flow in the surface streams, heavy mineralisation in boreholes, or latterly, the perennial problem in intensively farmed areas, nitrate pollution. **Dallas Dhu** and **Benromach** are no more, though the latter may soon reappear with a new water source.

Crossing the Great Glen Fault at the Kessock Bridge, we continue our northern journey. The water sources for the distilleries of the far north fall into two groups: those which percolate the Old Red Sandstone and those which drain the mountains formed of much older Moinian rocks to the west.

The first stop is just north of the ancient burgh of Tain, granted the rights of sanctuary in the eleventh century.

3 The Tarlogie Spring.

4 Old Red sandstones in the distillery buildings at Glenmorangie.

The Far North

'Where day contending with approaching Night
Assists the hero with continu'd Light.'
Edmund Waller, 1678.

It is a long journey to Wick, way north on the edge of the Ord of Caithness, where the scenery changes dramatically.

The land itself is flat lying and exposed; its boundary with the sea marked by high cliffs of grey-brown sandstones and shales. Master joints in the rock have been eroded by the sea to form deep, dark inlets called *geos*. We have moved from the alluvial plains of the Old Red Sandstone desert into the bed of the wide, shallow lake which formed this part of the Orcadian Basin.

The well-developed layering, or bedding, of these rocks means that they split into large, regular slabs or flagstones which have been transported south by sea to pave the streets of our great cities. They have other local uses: raised upright in rows as a substitute for fencing, or as more traditional stone walling. In the southeast of Wick are the stark, stone buildings of **Pulteney**, the most northerly distillery on the Scottish mainland. Described as the *Manzanilla of the North,* this highly distinctive, light, and some say salty, whisky now uses the town water supply pumped six kilometres south from the Loch of Yarrows. The old lade which carried water from Loch Hempriggs can still be followed until it disappears into the

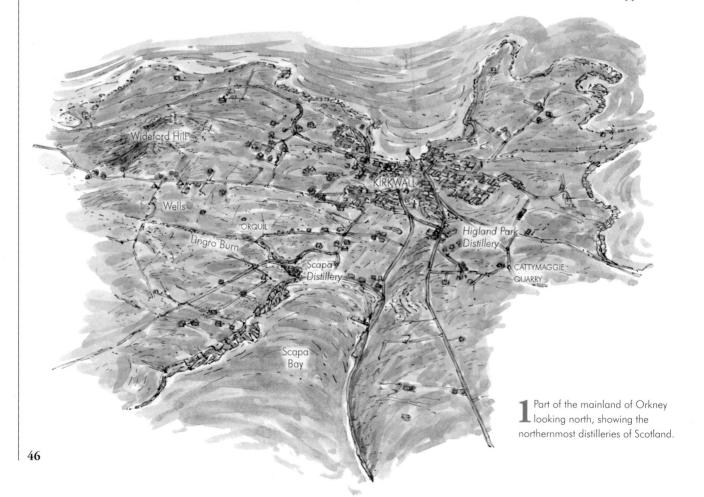

1 Part of the mainland of Orkney looking north, showing the northernmost distilleries of Scotland.

2 The flaggy rocks are used to build this bridge over the Lingro Burn.

where similar scenery to Caithness carved from flat-lying sandstones and shales, is epitomised in the *Old Man of Hoy.* On the largest island, confusingly called Mainland, the distilleries of **Scapa** and **Highland Park** compete for the title of most northerly. Geographically, Highland Park wins by almost a kilometre, but geologically it is the water source of Scapa which is furthest north (1).

Scapa distillery sits on the cliffs at the west of Scapa Bay next to the Lingro Burn (2), overlooking Scapa Flow, that great natural harbour used by the Home Fleet in two world wars. The burn is now only used as cooling water. The process waters are derived from three springs (4) in the flat-lying land beyond Orquil

distillery through a hole in the wall. To get to the most northerly distilleries we have to travel to the Isles of Orkney

4 One of the three springs from which Scapa draws its process waters.

3 Cattymaggie Quarry; the main water source for Highland Park.

Farm, about two kilometres to the west. Highland Park distillery is positioned on top of a north–south fault scarp on the southern edge of the city of Kirkwall. Here is another distillery that is proud of its hard water.

Being near the summit of a hill may present problems concerning the volumes of water required for distillation, but fortunately if the main source at Cattymaggie Quarry (3) gets low, there is another in the valley that can be used as a substitute. Low-necked stills, heathery peat and this special water combine to produce a dark, sweet aromatic dram.

The Far North

(On the Highlands) *'Miles and miles and miles of mere heather and peat and rocks'*
Matthew Arnold, 1864.

Having travelled to the Orkneys and reached the most northerly point of our journey we must now retrace our steps and return southwards to Inverness by almost the same route, taking in those distilleries we bypassed for geological reasons on our way north.

Leaving Helmsdale, going south, we soon realise that the flat land and high cliffs of Caithness have gone and a narrow coastal plain starts to appear, widening to four kilometres at the mouth of the River Brora. The greyish white sandstone town of Brora stands at the river mouth, set in fertile arable and pasture land.

As the building stones of the town indicate, the rocks here are unique to this part of Scotland. The land is underlain by a small area of relatively youthful *Jurassic* sandstones and shales *(see column on page 7)* within which are *coal seams,* the main reason a distillery was founded here. Coal: smelly and sulphurous, was mined here from the early 16th century until 1974, making it the most northerly coalfield in Britain. Despite its domestic shortcomings, the presence of cheap fuel, already used to fire brick kilns and evaporate salt from sea water, convinced the Earl of Stafford (later to become the Duke of Sutherland) in the early 19th century that an official distillery would be an excellent way of using his tenants' barley and would stop all the illegal distilling in the area.

The fossiliferous limestones and shales (1) can be seen on the sea shore, but by far the most impressive way to see the Jurassic rocks is to view the sandstones used to build Dunrobin Castle just to the north of Golspie.

Whilst the distilleries are on Jurassic rocks, the waters come from the Old Red Sandstone hills that rise abruptly to the west, raised up by the Helmsdale Fault, which runs parallel to the coast. Thus these uniquely golden, full-bodied, sweet whiskies are yet another Old Red Sandstone distillate!

Names can be confusing: the original Brora distillery, which used water from the Clyne Burn which flowed past it, produced whisky called **Clynelish** from its start until 1969. The building of the new Clynelish distillery required a more dependable source. This was and is the Clynemilton Burn which flows off the bare red

Lima concentrica

Echioceras tardecrescens

Cardioceras densiplicatum

1 Some Jurassic fossils from Brora, from the British Geological Survey collection, Keyworth.

sandstone slopes of Col Bheinn, to a dam in the hills from which it is gravity-fed to the distillery. The older distillery then produced **Brora** from 1975 to 1983.

South of Golspie we see again the familiar red sandstones of the southern part of the Orcadian Basin. Crossing the Dornoch Firth we turn west along its edge for four kilometres to reach the village of Edderton and the distillery of **Balblair.** The buildings lie on the same red sandstones as its near neighbour, Glenmorangie, but its waters come from even further west, from the bleak peat-covered mountains inland. *'Through peat over granite'* — we often heard this south of the Great Glen, but in the north it is unique. The waters of the Allt Dearg drain the peaty soils of the *Fearn Granite*, another Caledonian intrusion similar to those we saw in the Grampians. Water is diverted from the Allt Dearg into other streams so that eventually it makes its way to the distillery. Sweet and lightly peated, Balblair is the only granite-derived spirit north of the Great Glen.

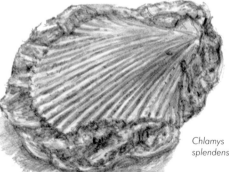

Chlamys splendens

We retrace our steps and continue south past Glenmorangie to the northern shores of the Cromarty Firth. Past the mighty grain distillery at Invergordon, we reach Alness, a beautifully situated town at the mouth of the river of the same name, where there are two distilleries which provide us with an opportunity to assess the effects of different waters. **Teaninich** draws waters from springs in the hills of Old Red Sandstone to the south, whilst **Dalmore** diverts water from a weir on the Alness River itself (3). This river has sources deep inland where the heather-covered peat is underlain by the 1100 million-year-old grey quartzites of the Moinian. The differences? Try them.

The A9 crosses the Cromarty Firth about ten kilometres south of Alness, but we will follow the edge of the Firth to

3 The weir on the River Alness which diverts water to Dalmore distillery.

2 High in these hills are the two lochs which form the source for the Ord distillery.

Dingwall on the A862 and continue to Muir of Ord and the **Glen Ord** distillery. To the west of it, in a flat area amongst the hills (2), lie two lochs, Loch nam Bonnach and Loch nam Eun. Reputedly the water in each is different and it is the coming together of these to form the White Burn *(Allt Fionnaidh)* that makes the amber-coloured, rich and lightly peated spirit so unmistakable.

Since we left Inverness we have travelled over 500 kilometres and it is to Inverness we now return at the end of this excursion.

The Far North

1 One of the most fashionable of the Victorian spas in Scotland was Strathpeffer. Here at the Pump House sulphurous waters were drawn from the *Fetid* or *Spa beds* of the Old Red Sandstone.

2 A doorway in the spectacular multicolour cathedral of St Magnus in Kirkwall. The whole building is constructed from locally quarried yellow *(Eday)* and red *(Head of Holland)* sandstones.

3 Tarradale House, on the shores of the Beauly Firth, was the birthplace of Roderick Impey Murchison (1792–1871) who amongst all his other geological and geographical achievements, was Director-General of the Geological Survey from 1855 until his death. The illustration is after a cartoon from *Punch Magazine*, September 23, 1865.

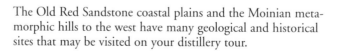

The Old Red Sandstone coastal plains and the Moinian metamorphic hills to the west have many geological and historical sites that may be visited on your distillery tour.

4 The gold prospectors' camp at Baille an Or in 1869. This village sprang up near the junction of the Kildonan Burn and the Helmsdale River during a short-lived *gold rush*. The river and the gold are still there!

5 A geo just to the south of Wick. The ruins of the castle of Old Wick are on the right-hand promontory.

6 Sueno's Stone, Forres. One of the largest (eight metres high) and best of the beautifully carved Pictish stones dating from the ninth century AD. The fine-grained red sandstone will take and retain detailed carving.

The Deep South

*'Freedom an' Whisky gang thegither,
Tak aff your dram!'*
Robert Burns, *Author's Earnest Cry.*

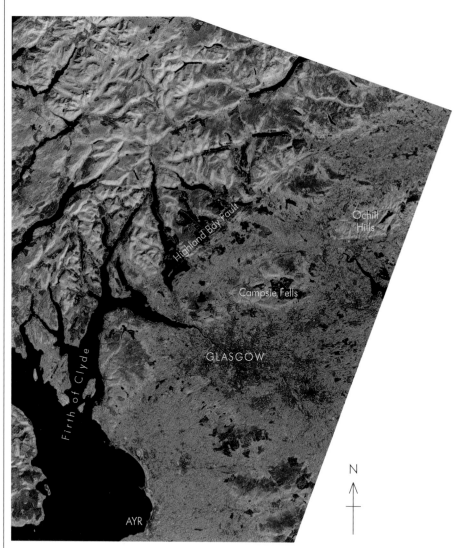

1 The false colour infrared satellite image shows the remarkable change from the Grampian Highlands to the Midland Valley (*Deep South*) across the Highland Line or Highland Boundary Fault. The orange-red colour in the south is agricultural land; water is black; forests brown. Small snowfields (*bright red*) can be seen on the northern slopes of mountains around Glencoe (*top left*). Turn the page upside down for a better appreciation of the relief. (*BGS enhanced satellite image*).

Location map of the Deep South.

The area lying to the south of the Highland Boundary Fault and to the north of the Southern Upland Fault (which runs from Glen App in the west to Dunbar in the east) is called the *Lowlands* or *Midland Valley*. Geologically it is a deep rift valley in which the land between the faults has sunk in relation to the upland blocks. However, this does not mean the whole area is low lying; far from it, the topography is very varied and there are some major ranges of hills (1).

Just south of the Highland Boundary Fault, in a belt running from southern Loch Lomond to Montrose, the red walls and fertile brown soils immediately remind us that we are back in Old Red Sandstone territory (2). Further south between Ayr, Glasgow and Edinburgh, younger *Carboniferous* rocks (*see column*

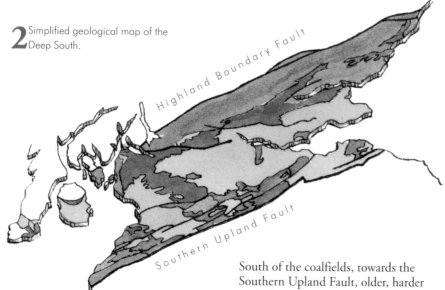

2 Simplified geological map of the Deep South.

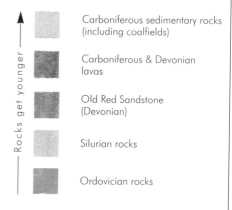

The Deep South

Rocks get younger →

Carboniferous sedimentary rocks (including coalfields)

Carboniferous & Devonian lavas

Old Red Sandstone (Devonian)

Silurian rocks

Ordovician rocks

on page 7) are represented by limestones, shales and the coalfields of Ayrshire, the Central region and Fife/Midlothian. Here the land is lower, particularly around the Forth valley and estuary where the soils are grey and less fertile.

North of the coalfields are the spectacular lava hills of Renfrewshire, the Kilpatricks, the Campsie Fells and the Gargunnocks of Carboniferous age and the Ochils and Sidlaws which are Devonian. Volcanic *plugs, bosses* and *sills* abound: at Dumbarton Rock, Dumbuck and Dumgoyne in the west; Stirling Rock and Abbey Craig in the centre; and of course, Castle Rock and Arthur's Seat in Edinburgh; and the Bass Rock in the Forth Estuary.

South of the coalfields, towards the Southern Upland Fault, older, harder rocks form hills such as the Pentlands south of Edinburgh. These are made up of more Devonian lavas and sedimentary rocks together with highly folded and very hard *Silurian* shales.

The mighty River Forth rises in the northwest beyond the Highland Boundary Fault and flows eastwards to enter the North Sea in the Firth of Forth. The other great river of the area, the Clyde, rises in the Southern Uplands and flows northwest to its estuary just south of the Highland Line.

A very large proportion of the population of Scotland lives within the Midland Valley and in places the wild hills compete with the claims of agriculture, housing and industrialisation. The pressure on water sources has meant that there is a continuing story of distillery closures, but some of the

greatest still remain and in this chapter we will visit them all.

The distilleries are divided geologically into two groups; those which draw their waters from the Dalradian rocks to the north of the Highland Boundary Fault and those that have a source south of the fault and which are thus truly southern.

Barley motif, Glengoyne.

The Deep South

A few pages and several hundred miles ago we imagined Queen Victoria and Prince Albert picnicking beside the distillery dam at Royal Lochnagar. Balmoral was their favourite residence and whilst there they made many forays into the surrounding countryside. One such in 1861, the last year of the Prince Consort's life, was to the town of Fettercairn in the heart of the fertile, barley-growing district of the Mearns, inland and to the north of Montrose. The population celebrated the visit by erecting a fine, though slightly idiosyncratic, arch of red sandstone across the main street *(page 59)*.

History does not tell us whether the Queen visited the **Fettercairn** distillery (1) there, but we can, and indeed we must, for this unusual, and all too-easily drinkable,

light malt continues to pour from the stills as it has done since 1824. Granite-sourced mountain waters from north of the Highland Boundary Fault flow onto and under the red soils of the farmland to be captured at springs (2) not far from the distillery. Surrounded by fields of golden barley and with the high mountains to the north, this is a stunning location.

Eighty kilometres along the fault to the southwest is the spa town of Crieff. Just north of the town, at the foot of the mountains marking the fault, is the hamlet of Hosh and the distillery of **Glenturret**. The river that thunders past the buildings comes from the heights to the north where a reservoir, Loch Turret, extends into a bowl surrounded by high peaks (4). Pale, light and smooth, the

2 One of the wells in a field near Fettercairn.

whisky mirrors the airy and beautiful location of its water source.

Even further southwest, but still in the Old Red Sandstone, on the road between Stirling and Callander lies the small town of Doune. On the opposite side of the River Teith is what was once a cotton mill, but since the mid 1960s has been the **Deanston** distillery. At a weir some way above the distillery itself, the process waters are diverted from the river into a wide canal. The Teith is another river that rises in the mountains of Dalradian rocks north of the Highland Boundary Fault, this time from the heather-covered crags and slopes surrounding Lochs Katrine and Ard in the world-renowned *mini Alps*: the Trossachs. From these lochs the river flows south over the fault and across red sandstone on its way to Doune. In the summer, when the flow in the river is low, the flat-lying sandstones and shales stand out in the river bed below the distillery buildings (3)

1 The Highlands form a background to the Fettercairn distillery.

3 Deanston distillery from the banks of the River Teith.

And so to Alexandria just north of Dumbarton, where probably one of the least-known malt whiskies is produced using water from one of the two most famous lochs in Scotland. The whisky is **Inchmurrin**, named after an island in the loch, Loch Lomond *(see inside back cover)*. The very rare Lomond stills can be set to produce differing types of product; and there is a heavier, sweeter equivalent to Inchmurrin which is called **Old Rhosdhu**.

Famous not only for its *'bonny banks and bonny braes'* but geologically because the Highland Boundary Fault crosses the southern end in a series of islands, Loch Lomond is most spectacular when viewed

4 Loch Turret: water source of Glenturret.

from the shores looking north to Ben Lomond. Between its southern outflow and the north bank of the Clyde there are major grain distilleries, blending plants and many bonded warehouses in which whiskies from all over the country are stored to mature until sold.

Until the early 1990s a single malt of special sweetness and golden colour was quietly produced within the large grain distillery complex on the shores of the Clyde at Dumbarton. Production has ceased, but **Inverleven** can still be found by the diligent searcher.

The Deep South

In our quest for southern whiskies which take their water from south of the Highland Boundary Fault we must return to the northeast and the town of Brechin, 11 kilometres west of Montrose and only 12 kilometres south of Fettercairn. Beyond the park on the eastern edge of the red sandstone town is the **Glencadam** distillery, producing a rarely bottled, rich and lightly peated malt using water from the lushly vegetated Unthank Hills just to the northeast.

There was another Old Red Sandstone whisky made in the coastal town of Montrose, though the distillery closed finally in 1992. The imposing buildings of **Lochside** are still there as are some of the bonded stores. The water source was hard water from a borehole deep into the sandstones under the buildings, in a situation remarkably close to the sea and where the risk of drawing in saline water must have been high.

Due south now, crossing the Firth of Tay and then the Firth of Forth to the *Athens of the North*; Edinburgh, Scotland's capital. About 20 kilometres to the east of the city, nestling in the rolling farmland around Pencaitland is the **Glenkinchie** distillery. From the grey-brown soils and buildings of coarse sandstone, it is clear we are close to Midlothian coalfield. Where there is coal, there is fireclay and where there is fireclay there are bricks. This is why the buildings at Glenkinchie are so distinctive: fine reddish brown buildings with many of the lintels and window frames outlined in yellow bricks (2) and a beautiful red, metal-strapped, brick chimney.

Originally the water for the distillery was taken from the lively Kinchie Burn that flows between the buildings, but the usual problems encountered in farmed and populated lowlands resulted in a change to the clear bright water taken from Hopes Reservoir in the Lammermuir Hills (1). In fact this makes the whisky unique amongst those currently in production, not only because the water is derived from Silurian strata but also because it is the only water source south of the Southern Upland Fault.

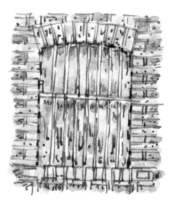

2 Detail of a brick warehouse at Glenkinchie Distillery.

1 Hopes Reservoir in the Lammermuir Hills: a Silurian source.

Westwards now, we go north of Glasgow to Dumgoyne, an old volcanic vent (3) on the edge of the lava plateau of the Kilpatrick Hills. We are in fact only a few miles from Dumbarton and Loch Lomond where we tarried on the previous page. At the foot of Dumgoyne, below a waterfall is the **Glengoyne** distillery (3) with its dam against a red sandstone cliff.

On the Clyde itself, **Auchentoshan**, the light, pale, *ladies malt,* and the now-closed **Littlemill** both used to draw their waters from the Kilpatricks but may have changed to the Glasgow supply from Loch Katrine, across the Highland Boundary Fault into the Dalradian.

Leaving the Midland Valley we go to the peninsula of Kintyre and to the town of Campbeltown. Once a great fishing port, with coal mines just to the north at Machrihanish, it was serviced regularly by the Clyde steamers; all that has gone. Thirty of the 32 distilleries have also disappeared, but the two that remain continue a process that was brought to this very spot by the Antrim Celts in the sixth century. Both distilleries hide

amongst the red sandstone houses in the centre of town. **Springbank**, pale in colour and sweet and creamy to taste, contrasts with **Glen Scotia**, a drier and more golden distillate. There is a third Campbeltown whisky, produced at the Springbank distillery and that is the very pungent, heavily peated **Longrow**.

Both distilleries use the town water supply, the Crosshill Loch (4), in the hills of Dalradian strata above the town, but each also has deep boreholes under the distillery. The Springbank Distillery, in common only with Glenfiddich, bottles its products at the distillery and thus its whiskies are reduced to bottling strength using the same water type as was used in the manufacture.

3 The lava plateau of the Campsie Fells with Dumgoyne, a volcanic vent *(centre right)*, and the Glengoyne Distillery below.

4 The Crosshill Loch with Campbeltown in the distance.

The Deep South

1 The much-quarried volcanic hill (*plug*) of Dumbuck towers over the whisky bonds (*secure warehouses*) with their 'guard geese'.

2 The Fountain of Nineveh, Bridge of Allan. Built in 1851, this cast iron fountain is one of a few reminders of the time when this town was a fashionable spa resort.

3 The 8th/9th century Pictish symbol-stone at Essie. Carved in local red sandstone, the interlaced patterns on the cross are characteristic of Christian art at that time. Above the cross is an angel and, below, a hunting scene showing a Pictish warrior armed with a spear, and various animals.

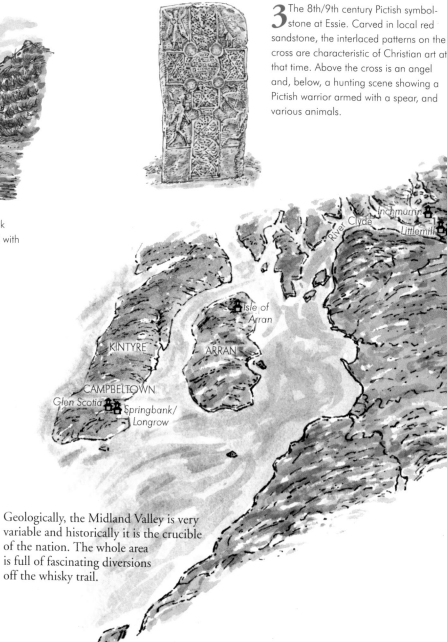

Geologically, the Midland Valley is very variable and historically it is the crucible of the nation. The whole area is full of fascinating diversions off the whisky trail.

4 This fine red sandstone arch in the centre of Fettercairn was built to commemorate the visit of Queen Victoria in 1861.

5 Kinnordy House near Kirriemuir was the birthplace of Sir Charles Lyell (1797–1875), a founding father of geology.

7 The Stone of Scone, the coronation stone of Scottish and English kings, is now in Edinburgh Castle. The rock itself looks similar to the red sandstone of the central region.

6 Red sandstones of Tantallon Castle contrast with the volcanic plug which forms the Bass Rock, just offshore.

The Wild West

'And rifted Rocks whose entrance leads to Hell,
For such there be, but unbelief is blind.'
John Milton, *Comus*.

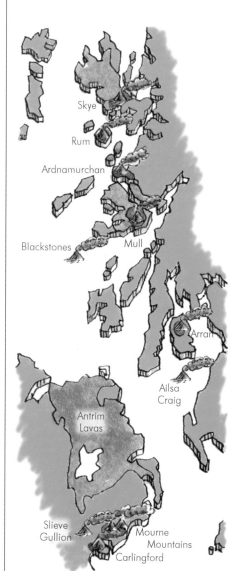

Granites etc. (old volcanic centres)

Lavas

We travelled a long way down the Kintyre peninsula to get to Campbeltown, but it is possible to go even further. A few miles to the south, just west of the village of Southend, the mighty Dalradian headland of the Mull of Kintyre rises out of the sea.

The view from the lighthouse at the Mull on a good day is stupendous, and, for many, surprising, for there, 20 kilometres across the North Channel, are the chalk cliffs of the Antrim coast of Northern Ireland. Few people realise how close they are.

Sailors have always been well aware of these narrows between the Atlantic Ocean to the north and the Irish Sea to the south, for here the waters can be wild and dangerous, particularly when the fast-flowing tides conflict with gale-force winds. The Celts also knew through their regular crossings in very small boats between Antrim, Kintyre and the Argyll Islands. The history and people of the three areas have always been closely related. Yes, we are back at last on the western seaboard of Scotland and we must go further west again to discover the last group of whiskies.

2 Location map of the Wild West elements.

Sixty or so million years ago, at the end of the Cretaceous Period, Britain, Europe and North America were still part of a *supercontinent* covered, in part, by a shallow, tropical sea. The calcareous muds deposited in this wide sea are now seen in the Chalk cliffs of southern England and Antrim.

It seemed that this part of the world would continue to be quiet for ever. But, as with all matters geological, this was an unwise assumption!

In the far northwest of the British Isles in the area described by the inshore waters forecast as *from Carlingford Lough to the Butt of Lewis* something was stirring; and it was stirring in a big way! Parts of the earth were beginning to move apart and

1 Schematic geological map showing the Wild West volcanoes still smoking.

the Atlantic Ocean as we know it today was starting to form. Strangely, this splitting approximately followed the line of the Caledonian mountains along which 'America' and 'Europe' collided to destroy an older ocean *(see page 21).*

The new ocean, the *Atlantic,* named after the giant *Atlas,* is thus the rebirth of the

Iapetus Ocean, named after the father of Atlas who was a titan in Greek mythology.

Greenland and America were moving away from Europe, forced apart by currents deep in the Earth's *mantle,* manifested on the surface as volcanoes along a series of fractures in the Earth's

crust. The area we are looking at started to move apart but never quite developed into the true mid-oceanic ridge which eventually formed to the west (2).

This process — the formation of oceans and *oceanic crust* is still continuing. Today it is Iceland that experiences all the fun of being astride a mid-oceanic ridge — free hot water comes with free volcanoes!

In a period of about 11 million years, between 63 and 52 million years ago, what we now know as the western edge of Scotland and parts of Northern Ireland were the focus of spectacular and violent volcanic activity (1). These are the Tertiary lavas in our column on page 7.

First, the earth started to split apart along many closely packed fractures. Out of the fractures poured liquid lava, millions and millions of cubic metres of it. It piled up layer upon layer until the individual flows had built up into a mass at least 800 metres in thickness. As in Iceland today, much of the lava oozed out steadily and quietly but, occasionally, huge explosions shattered the flows and formed layers of fragments and ash.

The lava flows were the precursor of even more impressive events: the establishment of huge volcanic cones looking much more like the traditional idea of a volcano.

Very spectacular, very dramatic — but how do we know?

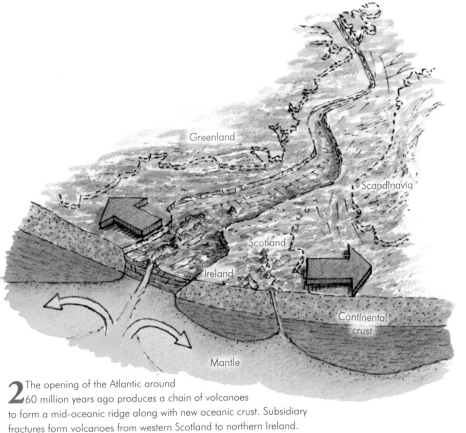

2 The opening of the Atlantic around 60 million years ago produces a chain of volcanoes to form a mid-oceanic ridge along with new oceanic crust. Subsidiary fractures form volcanoes from western Scotland to northern Ireland.

The Wild West

'Out where the smile dwells a little longer,
That's where the West begins.'
Arthur Chapman, *Out where the West begins.*

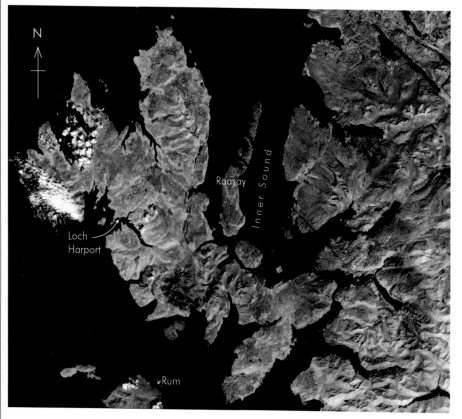

1 The Island of Skye from space. The false-colour, infrared image shows water as black and forests brown. The old volcanic centre is dominated by the Cuillin hills, made of gabbro, which shows up dark with snowfields *(red)*. The Red Hills, made of granite, show rocky tops *(pale blue)*; the north of the island is made of lava flows. For some readers, turning the picture upside down may give a better appreciation of the relief. *(BGS enhanced satellite image).*

The answer to the question on the previous page is: *because the evidence is still there for us to see and understand.*

So as you visit the distilleries and drink your whisky, look around.

In the northern parts of Skye and Mull and over a large part of Antrim, the landscape is made up of layer after layer of almost-horizontal *plateau basalts*, the fine-grained, dark lavas that were formed during the early stages of the breakup

which formed the Atlantic Ocean. The angular hills and deep valleys are the result of the erosion of these volcanic rocks. It is often possible to pick out each lava flow because many of them were exposed on the surface long enough for tropical weathering to start and a layer of red iron-rich laterite to develop *(page 67)*.

On the island of Staffa, off the western end of Mull, and on the Antrim coast near Ballycastle, the slow cooling of deep pools of lava resulted in the formation of the near-perfect columns which form structures famous throughout the world: *Fingal's Cave* on Staffa and the *Giant's Causeway* on the Antrim coast. Tradition has it that the two areas represent the foundations of a bridge that was being built by giants between the two coasts. The reality is even more stunning than the legend.

What of the huge volcanoes? The remains are everywhere. Erosion has removed the rocks that were on or near the surface and exposed the remains of the magma *chambers*. The coarse-grained rocks of these chambers form many of the region's most dramatic features.

On Skye we see *'the Ride of the Valkyries frozen in stone'* or, for the more down-to-earth, the great, jagged, black, gabbro mountains of the Cuillin which contrast markedly with the smooth, rounded, granite Red Hills to the east and south (1)

The old volcanoes also form the main peaks of Rum, Ardnamurchan, Mull and Arran in Scotland, the Mourne Mountains and Slieve Gullion in Northern Ireland

2 Loch Harport and the Talisker distillery from the southeast. The process waters are draw from springs in the lava flows capping Cnoc nan Speireag (left).

and at Carlingford just across the border in the Irish Republic *(see page 61)*. The remains of other ancient volcanoes are known to exist in the wild waters of the Atlantic. St Kilda still rises aggressively out of the sea, whilst closer to the mainland, to the west of Colonsay, the Blackstones are completely submerged. Further south the microgranite island of Ailsa Craig, *Paddy's milestone,* lies off the Ayrshire coast and has been the source of curling stones for many years.

And the distilleries? — there are three, each an individual but linked by a bond of fire which is reflected in the bright, spicy spirits that exude from their stills.

To the north is the **Talisker** distillery (2) at Carbost in the west of Skye, in a part described by Dr Johnson as *'the sort of place where a hermit might expect to grow old in meditation, without the probability of disturbance or interruption'.*

He must have seen Talisker itself on a very bad day, describing it as *'the place, beyond all that I have seen, from which the gay and the jovial seem utterly excluded.'*

He was there of course before the distillery, and the long journey is nowadays well justified. The buildings nestle on the sheltered shores of Loch Harport and use water from springs in the lava flows on the slopes of Cnoc nan Speireag which rises behind them. Through the distillery flows the Carbost Burn which provides the cooling waters.

Highland cattle.

63

*T*he *W*ild *W*est

*'...but ere the world shall come to an end,
Iona shall be as it was.'* St Columba, *attrib.*

Just over 80 kilometres due south of Talisker is the beautiful town of Tobermory. A port and tourist centre, it clings to the shore on the northeast of the island of Mull. At the southern end of the town, with its brightly painted sea-front houses, lies our second distillery (1).

Situated close to the shore, it has been producing its pale, dry spirits on and off for well over 100 years. It was silent for 42 years between 1930 and 1972, and then worked between 1972 and 1975, and from 1979 to 1981. Reopened in 1989, it is still working to produce a malt now called **Tobermory**. Some stocks of the earlier distillations are sold under the name **Ledaig**.

Like Skye, Mull is one of the largest of the islands of the Inner Hebrides and the continuing studies of its geology have been seminal in the development of the understanding of present and past volcanic activity.

In the south of the island is a huge *central complex*, the roots of an old volcano and, stretching out to the west and north, and extending as far as the mainland of Morvern, are the plateau basalts similar to those we have already seen on the north of Skye.

The topography of northern Mull is reminiscent of Skye though on a slightly smaller scale. Tobermory itself sits below a cliff formed of basalts and, a kilometre or so inland, near the Misnish Lochs, is a dam where the peaty waters are collected from the surrounding hills and piped to the distillery.

Nowhere are the plateau basalts better seen than in the world-famous cliffs on the island of Staffa, just off Mull's west coast. Here, Fingal's Cave amazed Victorian travellers and inspired Mendelssohn's *Hebridean Overture*.

There is another island off the coast of Mull — the holy island of Iona. It was here in 563 AD that the Celtic Christian, St Columba, landed from Ireland to set up a mission. It is rumoured that he also passed on the secrets of distillation. He is remembered in Scotland, but he is also commemorated in his homeland of Ireland.

In the Irish form, his name has been given to a small stream, St Columb's Rill (3), that flows across an even-more-extensive area of plateau basalts, those of Antrim in Northern Ireland. Nothing very significant about this, you might think, until it is revealed that the stream has, for nearly 400 years, been the water source for the **Bushmills** distillery (2) near Ballycastle on the northern coast. Founded in 1608, it is the earliest licenced distillery in the British Isles, and it is no more than ten kilometres from the greatest of all the cliffs of columnar basalt, the Giant's Causeway.

Spelling its name the Irish way, the malt *whiskey* produced here has the smooth

1 The distillery (*centre*) and houses painted in a rainbow of colours makeup the old part of the town of Tobermory.

Land of the Giants

2 Bushmills: the distillery buildings are highlighted by the distinctive red paintwork.

Wild? — at certain times of year.

West? — certainly, for we are not just on the edge of Scotland, we are on the edge of Europe.

Here, more than anywhere else on our tour, *Earth, Fire, Water* and *Wind* have come together to produce uniquely characteristic distillates.

Here, at the edge of the wild Atlantic where we started, we end our geotrail on the spot where the story of whisky began.

freshness that only triple distillation can produce. The malted barley used is only very lightly peated but the spicy richness of the finished product draws it together with its two Scottish counterparts. The only way to appreciate these spirits is to try all three together.

3 Bushmills: St Columb's Rill winds its way towards the distillery through the fertile soils of north Antrim.

The Wild West

Norse and Celtic heritages merge in Ireland and the islands of the West. Here the great Atlantic has shaped lands rich in folklore and fable.

2 The columnar basalts of Fingal's Cave on the Isle of Staffa provided the inspiration for Mendelssohn's *Hebridean Overture*.

1 The granite of Ailsa Craig is traditionally used to make curling stones.

3 Central Skye looking southwest from the island of Raasay. The jagged, gabbroic Cuillin hills are in the distance in cloud. Closer *(centre and right)* are the rounded Red Hills made of granite.

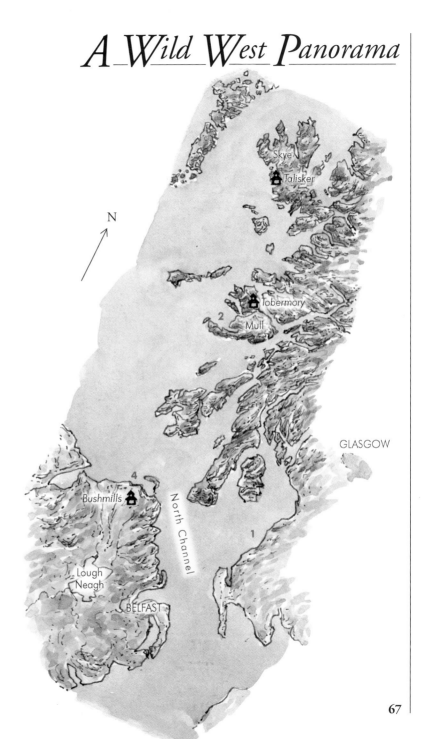

4 Above the Giant's Causeway on the Antrim coast rise the Giant's Harp and the Chimney Tops. These are two separate basalts lava flows with columnar jointing in their lower parts. The basalts lie on top of earlier lava flows which were weathered to a reddish laterite.

N

Skye

Talisker

Tobermory

Mull

2

GLASGOW

4

Bushmills

North Channel

1

Lough Neagh

BELFAST

Lost and to be Found

1 The fine red sandstone maltings at Blackford, now the home of the Gleneagles Spring Water Company.

It is always sad when a distillery closes, even temporarily. Often the closure is not noticed immediately, except by those directly affected, for it may be 10 or 15 years before its products start to disappear, and in the intervening period, unless it is demolished, there is always a chance that it may reopen in more favourable times.

The bare fact is that although surrounded by romance, legend and tradition, the distillation of these unique spirits is an incredibly successful commercial operation and as such it has to be run on economic and not emotional guidelines.

Over the last 150 years a very large number of distilleries have lived, blossomed and died; Campbeltown once had 40 and the Lowlands had many more than now.

For our journey the saddest of all is a loss, not only of a unique spirit but of the opportunity to look at a specific geological setting not seen elsewhere. Such is **Bladnoch** — so far south that had it been on the east coast it would have been just north of Durham! It is actually just south of Wigtown on the coast in the extreme southwest of Dumfries and Galloway. It was the most southerly malt whisky distillery in the United Kingdom, even further south than Bushmills. Its waters were uniquely sourced from the gently rolling lowlands and crumbly brown soils of the Ordovician and Silurian shales of the Southern Upland. It was also the only malt distillery ever to operate south of the Southern Upland Fault. The buildings remain as a museum and a site of pilgrimage for those seeking the source of this light and fruity Lower Palaeozoic whisky.

Further north, we shall never again see spirity **St Magdalene** from the Carboniferous lavas around Linlithgow or the pale **Rosebank** of Falkirk, which took its water from the Carron Valley Reservoir, the town supply in the Carboniferous lavas of the Campsie Fells to the west.

At Blackford on the A9 north of Stirling there is still hope for **Tullibardine,** a delightfully soft and spicy malt. The water source, the Danny Burn, which runs north from the Devonian lavas of the Ochils, originally supplied a brewery where, in 1488, James IV of Scotland refreshed himself after his coronation at Scone.

Water is still important at Blackford, for here is the modern bottling plant of *Highland Spring* mineral water; a bit of a misnomer as we are still 25 kilometres south of the Highland Line. Here too is the *Gleneagles Spring Water Company* (1) taking water from the Old Red Sandstone beneath the old maltings. Take the opportunity to study the fine red building stone with the more workable Carboniferous sandstones around the windows.

The most interesting losses on Speyside are **Parkmore** (2) at Dufftown and **Glenglassaugh** on the northeast coast just west of Portsoy. Both selected water sources derived from the local Dalradian limestones and there were always serious problems. Parkmore closed many years ago though its buildings are still in regular use. Glenglassaugh has had varying fortunes, at one point resorting to importing water from elsewhere. At present it is mothballed.

Lost and to be Found

2 Parkmore Distillery at Dufftown.

ends. But in reality for all of us it has only just begun; a complete knowledge of whisky cannot be gained in a single lifetime — the key is to spend a lifetime trying to gain it!

So, let old distilleries tap the young rocks and new distilleries the old; let the water of life refresh you now, and for ever.

Slainthe!

On the other hand the birth of a completely new distillery is a major event and the cause of much celebration and anticipation. Like that of a child itself, the birth may be exciting, but the real joy is to watch the infant develop towards maturity.

The **Isle of Arran** distillery (3) started distilling in 1995 on the north coast of the island at Lochranza. Around the Millenium it will release the first single malt which will take its place proudly beside the other whiskies of the west. The water source, the Easan Biorach, flows dramatically down from the Tertiary granite which makes up the hills that tower behind the buildings. These are the roots of a great volcano.

And so after over 100 distilleries and many hundreds of miles, our journey

3 The new Isle of Arran Distillery at Lochranza.

*M*alt *W*hisky *I*ndex

Page numbers in roman refer to the text; numbers in *italics* refer to relevant illustrations.

Geological Glossary

Anticline — an arch structure in the strata with older rocks in the core.

Basalt — a dark, fine-grained, *igneous* rock; a cooled *magma* from the Earth's *mantle.*

Basin — a depressed area with no surface outlet for water.

Conglomerate — a rock of consolidated pebbles or boulders.

Crust — the outermost layer of the Earth which lies above the *mantle;* its thickness averages around 35 kilometres. It is divided into active plates.

Dolomite — a *sedimentary* rock rich in magnesium carbonate.

Dyke — an *igneous* rock body which tends to cut the strata vertically.

Fault — a fracture in the rock causing relative displacement between one side and the other.

Gabbro — a dark, coarse-grained, *igneous* rock; a cooled *magma* from the Earth's mantle.

Geo — a long, deep, narrow, coastal inlet or cove.

Gneiss — a coarse-grained, highly-*metamorphosed* rock resembling a streaky or banded *granite.*

Granite — a pale or pink, coarse-grained, *igneous* rock comprising mainly quartz and feldspar speckled with mica.

Greenstone — a *basalt* or dolerite *metamorphosed* to produce green minerals.

Grit — a coarse sand.

Igneous — refers to rock or mineral crystallised from a *magma.*

Limestone — a *sedimentary* rock rich in calcium carbonate.

Magma — a liquid rock generated at high temperatures in the *mantle* or *crust* of the Earth.

Mantle — the layer in the Earth below the *crust* and above the core.

Marble — *metamorphosed limestone.*

Metamorphism — the changes in minerals, chemistry and structure of a rock subjected to different temperatures and pressures, particularly during an *orogeny.*

Migmatite — a mixed rock caused by the melting of *granite* in high-grade *metamorphic* rocks

Mudstones — a rock of consolidated mud.

Nappe — a mass of rock pushed or thrust over another, normally during *orogeny.*

Orogeny — formation of mountains through collision of *crustal* plates.

Quartzite — *metamorphosed sandstone:* a hard, dense, usually white, quartz rock.

Phyllite — *metamorphosed mudstone* with a glinting micaceous sheen.

Plug — a vertical volcanic vent or pipe, usually eroded.

Rift valley — a regional feature where the valley forms by subsidence along *faults.*

Sandstone — a rock of consolidated sand.

Schist — strongly *metamorphosed mudstone* with a glittering micaceous sheen.

Shale — a rock of consolidated mud and silt.

Sedimentary — refers to a rock formed by erosion and deposition, especially in water.

Sill — an *igneous* rock body which tends to lie horizontally within the strata.

Silt — very fine sand.

Slate — weakly *metamorphosed mudstone* with a strong parting or cleavage.

Till — the deposits of glaciers.

Of Further Interest

Acknowledgments

We have always received a warm welcome from the distillery managers we have visited over the last few years. To them and their counterparts at the various head offices we wish to give our thanks. The writing of much of this book would have been impossible without their help and assistance. To name them all would take a book itself, but in particular we would like to mention Trevor Cowan, Richard Paterson and James McEwan. We also thank Trevor for his permission to use the quotation on page 27.

On the geological side, we thank particularly, David Stephenson of the British Geological Survey in Edinburgh for his advice and assistance, especially concerning the Grampians and the geology-based figures on pages 32–37.

Lastly, our thanks go to Roger Ellis of *Mining Journal*, who started the whole ball rolling in 1989, little realising where it would end up.

Further Reading

The British Geological Survey (BGS) produces **geological maps** (1:50 000 and 1: 250 000 scales) and **memoirs** for Scotland. **Regional guides** are also published for Orkney and Shetland; the Northern Highlands; the Tertiary Volcanic Districts; the Grampian Highlands, the Midland Valley; and the South of Scotland. The BGS and the Scottish National Heritage have combined to produce a **popular series** subtitled *A Landscape fashioned by Geology*. Titles include Arran & Clyde Islands, Caingorms, East Lothian & Borders, Edinburgh, Loch Lomond–Stirling, Orkney & Shetland and Skye. *These publications can be obtained from the BGS offices (right) or the main sales desk (page 71).*

Geology of Scotland edited by G Y Craig, 1991. (London: Geological Society). *An introduction to the geology of the whole of Scotland.*

The Malt Whisky File by John Lamond and Robin Tucek, 1997. (Edinburgh: Canongate Books). *A regularly updated book describing in detail the flavour and taste of malt whiskies.*

Michael Jackon's Malt Whisky Companion by Michael Jackson, 1994. (London: Dorling Kindersley). *Another excellent guide to the appreciation of fine malt whiskies.*

Useful Contacts

The British Geological Survey offices are open for geological consultations. Addresses:

Murchison House,
West Mains Road,
Edinburgh EH9 3LA
Tel 0131 667 1000
Fax 0131 668 2683

Kingsley Dunham Centre,
Keyworth,
Nottingham NG12 5GG
Tel 0115 936 3100
Fax 0115 936 3200

BGS London Information Office,
Natural History Museum
Earth Galleries,
Exhibition Road,
South Kensington,
London SW7 2DE
Tel 0171 589 4090
Fax 0171 584 8270

The Scotch Whisky Association will supply a reading list, maps, brochures and general information about whisky manufacture, distilleri and many other aspects. Addresses:

14 Cork Street,
London W1X 1PF
Tel 0171 629 4384
Fax 0171 493 1398

20 Atholl Crescent,
Edinburgh EH3 8H
Tel 0131 222 9200
Fax 0131 228 8971

The Scotch Malt Whisky Society selects for its members highly individual single casks of Scotch Malt Whisky which it bottles without dilution o chill filtration. Information on individual bottle is then made available to members through regular bottling lists and further news on whisky is published through a newsletter. Address:

The Vaults,
87 Giles Street,
Leith,
Edinburgh EH6 6BZ
Tel 0131 555 2266
Fax 0131 553 1003

The Scotch Whisky Heritage Centre is situatec beside Edinburgh Castle and is committed to telling the story of Scotch Whisky. A tour of the centre employs advanced presentation technique in eight different languages and concludes with a free dram and a visit to the gift shop, where a collection of malt and blended whiskies — some of them very rare — are displayed for sale, together with a selection of relevant books etc. Address:

354 Castlehill,
The Royal Mile,
Edinburgh EH1 2NE
Tel 0131 220 6288
Fax 0131 220 6288